VOL **12** LOG-MET
967–1054

FUNK & WAGNALLS **new**
ENCYCLOPEDIA
OF SCIENCE

FUNK & WAGNALLS, INC.

HOW TO USE FUNK & WAGNALLS NEW ENCYCLOPEDIA OF SCIENCE

Volumes 1 through 21 have information printed on the front covers, spine, and title pages that make it easy to find the articles you want to read.

- Volume numbers are printed in all three places in Volumes 1 through 21.
- Letter breaks — $\frac{COL}{DIA}$ — are printed in all three places in Volumes 1 through 21. The letters above the line are the first three letters of the first article title in the volume. The letters below the line are the first three letters of the last article title in the volume.
- Page breaks — $\frac{351}{438}$ — are printed on the spines and title pages of Volumes 1 through 21. They provide the page numbers of the first and last text pages in the volume.

Articles are arranged alphabetically by title in Volumes 1 through 21. Most titles are printed in **BOLD-FACE CAPITAL** letters. Some titles are printed in even larger letters.

- Some titles are not article titles, but refer you to the actual article title. Within articles you will find *See* or *See also* other article names for further information. All of these references to other articles are called cross-references.
- Most article titles are followed by a phonetic pronunciation. Use the Pronunciation Guide on page vi of Volume 1 to learn the correct pronunciation of the article title.
- At the end of most articles are two sets of initials. The first set identifies the person who wrote the article. The second set identifies the special consultant who checked the article for accuracy. All of these people are listed by their initials and full names and position on pages v and vi of Volume 1.
- ◥ This symbol at the end of an article indicates that there is a project based on the subject of the article in the Projects, Bibliography & Index volume. The project is found under its article title, and all of the project article titles are arranged alphabetically on pages 1 through 64 of the Projects, Bibliography & Index volume.

The Projects, Bibliography & Index Volume contains three sections. Each is an essential part of the encyclopedia.

- Projects based on articles in the encyclopedia are found in the first section. Each is both entertaining and educational. Each is designed for use by a student and for parental participation if desired.
- Bibliography reading lists in the second section list books under general scientific categories that are also titles of major articles. Each book listed is marked with either a YA (Young Adult) or J (Juvenile) reading level indicator. YA generally applies to readers at the junior high level or higher. J applies to readers at grade levels below junior high school.
- Index entries for all article titles plus many subjects that are not article titles are found in the third section. Instructions on using the Index are found at the start of the Index section in the Projects, Bibliography & Index volume.

LOGARITHM TABLES: Logarithms

	0	1	2	3	4	5	6	7	8	9	1	2	3	4	5	6	7	8	9
10	.0000	0043	0086	0128	0170	0212	0253	0294	0334	0374	4	8	12	17	21	25	29	33	37
11	.0414	0453	0492	0531	0569	0607	0645	0682	0719	0755	4	8	11	15	19	23	26	30	34
12	.0792	0828	0864	0899	0934	0969	1004	1038	1072	1106	3	7	10	14	17	21	24	28	31
13	.1139	1173	1206	1239	1271	1303	1335	1367	1399	1430	3	6	10	13	16	19	23	26	29
14	.1461	1492	1523	1553	1584	1614	1644	1673	1703	1732	3	6	9	12	15	18	21	24	27
15	.1761	1790	1818	1847	1875	1903	1931	1959	1987	2014	3	6	8	11	14	17	20	22	25
16	.2041	2068	2095	2122	2148	2175	2201	2227	2253	2279	3	5	8	11	13	16	18	21	24
17	.2304	2330	2355	2380	2405	2430	2455	2480	2504	2529	2	5	7	10	12	15	17	20	22
18	.2553	2577	2601	2625	2648	2672	2695	2718	2742	2765	2	5	7	9	12	14	16	19	21
19	.2788	2810	2833	2856	2878	2900	2923	2945	2967	2989	2	4	7	9	11	13	16	18	20
20	.3010	3032	3054	3075	3096	3118	3139	3160	3181	3201	2	4	6	8	11	13	15	17	19
21	.3222	3243	3263	3284	3304	3324	3345	3365	3385	3404	2	4	6	8	10	12	14	16	18
22	.3424	3444	3464	3483	3502	3522	3541	3560	3579	3598	2	4	6	8	10	12	14	15	17
23	.3617	3636	3655	3674	3692	3711	3729	3747	3766	3784	2	4	6	7	9	11	13	15	17
24	.3802	3820	3838	3856	3874	3892	3909	3927	3945	3962	2	4	5	7	9	11	12	14	16
25	.3979	3997	4014	4031	4048	4065	4082	4099	4116	4133	2	3	5	7	9	10	12	14	15
26	.4150	4166	4183	4200	4216	4232	4249	4265	4281	4298	2	3	5	7	8	10	11	13	15
27	.4314	4330	4346	4362	4378	4393	4409	4425	4440	4456	2	3	5	6	8	9	11	13	14
28	.4472	4487	4502	4518	4533	4548	4564	4579	4594	4609	2	3	5	6	8	9	11	12	14
29	.4624	4639	4654	4669	4683	4698	4713	4728	4742	4757	1	3	4	6	7	9	10	12	13
30	.4771	4786	4800	4814	4829	4843	4857	4871	4886	4900	1	3	4	6	7	9	10	11	13
31	.4914	4928	4942	4955	4969	4983	4997	5011	5024	5038	1	3	4	6	7	8	10	11	12
32	.5051	5065	5079	5092	5105	5119	5132	5145	5159	5172	1	3	4	5	7	8	9	11	12
33	.5185	5198	5211	5224	5237	5250	5263	5276	5289	5302	1	3	4	5	6	8	9	10	12
34	.5315	5328	5340	5353	5366	5378	5391	5403	5416	5428	1	3	4	5	6	8	9	10	11
35	.5441	5453	5465	5478	5490	5502	5514	5527	5539	5551	1	2	4	5	6	7	9	10	11
36	.5563	5575	5587	5599	5611	5623	5635	5647	5658	5670	1	2	4	5	6	7	8	10	11
37	.5682	5694	5705	5717	5729	5740	5752	5763	5775	5786	1	2	3	5	6	7	8	9	10
38	.5798	5809	5821	5832	5843	5855	5866	5877	5888	5899	1	2	3	5	6	7	8	9	10
39	.5911	5922	5933	5944	5955	5966	5977	5988	5999	6010	1	2	3	4	5	7	8	9	10
40	.6021	6031	6042	6053	6064	6075	6085	6096	6107	6117	1	2	3	4	5	6	8	9	10
41	.6128	6138	6149	6160	6170	6180	6191	6201	6212	6222	1	2	3	4	5	6	7	8	9
42	.6232	6243	6253	6263	6274	6284	6294	6304	6314	6325	1	2	3	4	5	6	7	8	9
43	.6335	6345	6355	6365	6375	6385	6395	6405	6415	6425	1	2	3	4	5	6	7	8	9
44	.6435	6444	6454	6464	6474	6484	6493	6503	6513	6522	1	2	3	4	5	6	7	8	9
45	.6532	6542	6551	6561	6571	6580	6590	6599	6609	6618	1	2	3	4	5	6	7	8	9
46	.6628	6637	6646	6656	6665	6675	6684	6693	6702	6712	1	2	3	4	5	6	7	7	8
47	.6721	6730	6739	6749	6758	6767	6776	6785	6794	6803	1	2	3	4	5	5	6	7	8
48	.6812	6821	6830	6839	6848	6857	6866	6875	6884	6893	1	2	3	4	4	5	6	7	8
49	.6902	6911	6920	6928	6937	6946	6955	6964	6972	6981	1	2	3	4	4	5	6	7	8
50	.6990	6998	7007	7016	7024	7033	7042	7050	7059	7067	1	2	3	3	4	5	6	7	8
51	.7076	7084	7093	7101	7110	7118	7126	7135	7143	7152	1	2	3	3	4	5	6	7	8
52	.7160	7168	7177	7185	7193	7202	7210	7218	7226	7235	1	2	2	3	4	5	6	7	7
53	.7243	7251	7259	7267	7275	7284	7292	7300	7308	7316	1	2	2	3	4	5	6	6	7
54	.7324	7332	7340	7348	7356	7364	7372	7380	7388	7396	1	2	2	3	4	5	6	6	7

LOGARITHM TABLES: Logarithms

	0	1	2	3	4	5	6	7	8	9	1	2	3	4	5	6	7	8	9
55	.7404	7412	7419	7427	7435	7443	7451	7459	7466	7474	1	2	2	3	4	5	5	6	7
56	.7482	7490	7497	7505	7513	7520	7528	7536	7543	7551	1	2	2	3	4	5	5	6	7
57	.7559	7566	7574	7582	7589	7597	7604	7612	7619	7627	1	2	2	3	4	5	5	6	7
58	.7634	7642	7649	7657	7664	7672	7679	7686	7694	7701	1	1	2	3	4	4	5	6	7
59	.7709	7716	7723	7731	7738	7745	7752	7760	7767	7774	1	1	2	3	4	4	5	6	7
60	.7782	7789	7796	7803	7810	7818	7825	7832	7839	7846	1	1	2	3	4	4	5	6	6
61	.7853	7860	7868	7875	7882	7889	7896	7903	7910	7917	1	1	2	3	4	4	5	6	6
62	.7924	7931	7938	7945	7952	7959	7966	7973	7980	7987	1	1	2	3	3	4	5	6	6
63	.7993	8000	8007	8014	8021	8028	8035	8041	8048	8055	1	1	2	3	3	4	5	5	6
64	.8062	8069	8075	8082	8039	8096	8102	8109	8116	8122	1	1	2	3	3	4	5	5	6
65	.8129	8136	8142	8149	8156	8162	8169	8176	8182	8189	1	1	2	3	3	4	5	5	6
66	.8195	8202	8209	8215	8222	8228	8235	8241	8248	8254	1	1	2	3	3	4	5	5	6
67	.8261	8267	8274	8280	8287	8293	8299	8306	8312	8319	1	1	2	3	3	4	5	5	6
68	.8325	8331	8338	8344	8351	8357	8363	8370	8376	8382	1	1	2	3	3	4	4	5	6
69	.8388	8395	8401	8407	8414	8420	8426	8432	8439	8445	1	1	2	2	3	4	4	5	6
70	.8451	8457	8463	8470	8476	8482	8488	8494	8500	8506	1	1	2	2	3	4	4	5	6
71	.8513	8519	8525	8531	8537	8543	8549	8555	8561	8567	1	1	2	2	3	4	4	5	5
72	.8573	8579	8585	8591	8597	8603	8609	8615	8621	8627	1	1	2	2	3	4	4	5	5
73	.8633	8639	8645	8651	8657	8663	8669	8675	8681	8686	1	1	2	2	3	4	4	5	5
74	.8692	8698	8704	8710	8716	8722	8727	8733	8739	8745	1	1	2	2	3	4	4	5	5
75	.8751	8756	8762	8768	8774	8779	8785	8791	8797	8802	1	1	2	2	3	3	4	5	5
76	.8808	8814	8820	8825	8831	8837	8842	8848	8854	8859	1	1	2	2	3	3	4	5	5
77	.8865	8871	8876	8882	8887	8893	8899	8904	8910	8915	1	1	2	2	3	3	4	4	5
78	.8921	8927	8932	8938	8943	8949	8954	8960	8965	8971	1	1	2	2	3	3	4	4	5
79	.8976	8982	8987	8993	8998	9004	9009	9015	9020	9025	1	1	2	2	3	3	4	4	5
80	.9031	9036	9042	9047	9053	9058	9063	9069	9074	9079	1	1	2	2	3	3	4	4	5
81	.9085	9090	9096	9101	9106	9112	9117	9122	9128	9133	1	1	2	2	3	3	4	4	5
82	.9138	9143	9149	9154	9159	9165	9170	9175	9180	9186	1	1	2	2	3	3	4	4	5
83	.9191	9196	9201	9206	9212	9217	9222	9227	9232	9238	1	1	2	2	3	3	4	4	5
84	.9243	9248	9253	9258	9263	9269	9274	9279	9284	9289	1	1	2	2	3	3	4	4	5
85	.9294	9299	9304	9309	9315	9320	9325	9330	9335	9340	1	1	2	2	3	3	4	4	5
86	.9345	9350	9355	9360	9365	9370	9375	9380	9385	9390	1	1	2	2	3	3	4	4	5
87	.9395	9400	9405	9410	9415	9420	9425	9430	9435	9440	0	1	1	2	2	3	3	4	4
88	.9415	9450	9455	9460	9465	9469	9474	9479	9484	9489	0	1	1	2	2	3	3	4	4
89	.9494	9499	9504	9509	9513	9518	9523	9528	9533	9538	0	1	1	2	2	3	3	4	4
90	.9542	9547	9552	9557	9562	9566	9571	9576	9581	9586	0	1	1	2	2	3	3	4	4
91	.9590	9595	9600	9605	9609	9614	9619	9624	9628	9633	0	1	1	2	2	3	3	4	4
92	.9638	9643	9647	9652	9657	9661	9666	9671	9675	9680	0	1	1	2	2	3	3	4	4
93	.9685	9689	9694	9699	9703	9708	9713	9717	9722	9727	0	1	1	2	2	3	3	4	4
94	.9731	9736	9741	9745	9750	9754	9759	9763	9768	9773	0	1	1	2	2	3	3	4	4
95	.9777	9782	9786	9791	9795	9800	9805	9809	9814	9818	0	1	1	2	2	3	3	4	4
96	.9823	9827	9832	9836	9841	9845	9850	9854	9859	9863	0	1	1	2	2	3	3	4	4
97	.9868	9872	9877	9881	9886	9890	9894	9899	9903	9908	0	1	1	2	2	3	3	4	4
98	.9912	9917	9921	9926	9930	9934	9939	9943	9948	9952	0	1	1	2	2	3	3	4	4
99	.9956	9961	9965	9969	9974	9978	9983	9987	9991	9996	0	1	1	2	2	3	3	3	4

For use of these tables, see LOGARITHM, pages 965–966.

LOGARITHM TABLES: Antilogarithms

	0	1	2	3	4	5	6	7	8	9	1	2	3	4	5	6	7	8	9
.00	1000	1002	1005	1007	1009	1012	1014	1016	1019	1021	0	0	1	1	1	1	2	2	2
.01	1023	1026	1028	1030	1033	1035	1038	1040	1042	1045	0	0	1	1	1	1	2	2	2
.02	1047	1050	1052	1054	1057	1059	1062	1064	1067	1069	0	0	1	1	1	1	2	2	2
.03	1072	1074	1076	1079	1081	1084	1086	1089	1091	1094	0	0	1	1	1	1	2	2	2
.04	1096	1099	1102	1104	1107	1109	1112	1114	1117	1119	0	1	1	1	1	2	2	2	2
.05	1122	1125	1127	1130	1132	1135	1138	1140	1143	1146	0	1	1	1	1	2	2	2	2
.06	1148	1151	1153	1156	1159	1161	1164	1167	1169	1172	0	1	1	1	1	2	2	2	2
.07	1175	1178	1180	1183	1186	1189	1191	1194	1197	1199	0	1	1	1	1	2	2	2	2
.08	1202	1205	1208	1211	1213	1216	1219	1222	1225	1227	0	1	1	1	1	2	2	2	3
.09	1230	1233	1236	1239	1242	1245	1247	1250	1253	1256	0	1	1	1	1	2	2	2	3
.10	1259	1262	1265	1268	1271	1274	1276	1279	1282	1285	0	1	1	1	1	2	2	2	3
.11	1288	1291	1294	1297	1300	1303	1306	1309	1312	1315	0	1	1	1	2	2	2	2	3
.12	1318	1321	1324	1327	1330	1334	1337	1340	1343	1346	0	1	1	1	2	2	2	2	3
.13	1349	1352	1355	1358	1361	1365	1368	1371	1374	1377	0	1	1	1	2	2	2	3	3
.14	1380	1384	1387	1390	1393	1396	1400	1403	1406	1409	0	1	1	1	2	2	2	3	3
.15	1413	1416	1419	1422	1426	1429	1432	1435	1439	1442	0	1	1	1	2	2	2	3	3
.16	1445	1449	1452	1455	1459	1462	1466	1469	1472	1476	0	1	1	1	2	2	2	3	3
.17	1479	1483	1486	1489	1493	1496	1500	1503	1507	1510	0	1	1	1	2	2	2	3	3
.18	1514	1517	1521	1524	1528	1531	1535	1538	1542	1545	0	1	1	1	2	2	2	3	3
.19	1549	1552	1556	1560	1563	1567	1570	1574	1578	1581	0	1	1	1	2	2	3	3	3
.20	1585	1589	1592	1596	1600	1603	1607	1611	1614	1618	0	1	1	1	2	2	3	3	3
.21	1622	1626	1629	1633	1637	1641	1644	1648	1652	1656	0	1	1	2	2	2	3	3	3
.22	1660	1663	1667	1671	1675	1679	1683	1687	1690	1694	0	1	1	2	2	2	3	3	3
.23	1698	1702	1706	1710	1714	1718	1722	1726	1730	1734	0	1	1	2	2	2	3	3	4
.24	1738	1742	1746	1750	1754	1758	1762	1766	1770	1774	0	1	1	2	2	2	3	3	4
.25	1778	1782	1786	1791	1795	1799	1803	1807	1811	1816	0	1	1	2	2	2	3	3	4
.26	1820	1824	1828	1832	1837	1841	1845	1849	1854	1858	0	1	1	2	2	3	3	3	4
.27	1862	1866	1871	1875	1879	1884	1888	1892	1897	1901	0	1	1	2	2	3	3	3	4
.28	1905	1910	1914	1919	1923	1928	1932	1936	1941	1945	0	1	1	2	2	3	3	4	4
.29	1950	1954	1959	1963	1968	1972	1977	1982	1986	1991	0	1	1	2	2	3	3	4	4
.30	1995	2000	2004	2009	2014	2018	2023	2028	2032	2037	0	1	1	2	2	3	3	4	4
.31	2042	2046	2051	2056	2061	2065	2070	2075	2080	2084	0	1	1	2	2	3	3	4	4
.32	2089	2094	2099	2104	2109	2113	2118	2123	2128	2133	0	1	1	2	2	3	3	4	4
.33	2138	2143	2148	2153	2158	2163	2168	2173	2178	2183	0	1	1	2	2	3	3	4	4
.34	2188	2193	2198	2203	2208	2213	2218	2223	2228	2234	1	1	2	2	3	3	4	4	5
.35	2239	2244	2249	2254	2259	2265	2270	2275	2280	2286	1	1	2	2	3	3	4	4	5
.36	2291	2296	2301	2307	2312	2317	2323	2328	2333	2339	1	1	2	2	3	3	4	4	5
.37	2344	2350	2355	2360	2366	2371	2377	2382	2388	2393	1	1	2	2	3	3	4	4	5
.38	2399	2404	2410	2415	2421	2427	2432	2438	2443	2449	1	1	2	2	3	3	4	4	5
.39	2455	2460	2466	2472	2477	2483	2489	2495	2500	2506	1	1	2	2	3	3	4	5	5
.40	2512	2518	2523	2529	2535	2541	2547	2553	2559	2564	1	1	2	2	3	4	4	5	5
.41	2570	2576	2582	2588	2594	2600	2606	2612	2618	2624	1	1	2	2	3	4	4	5	5
.42	2630	2636	2642	2649	2655	2661	2667	2673	2679	2685	1	1	2	2	3	4	4	5	6
.43	2692	2698	2704	2710	2716	2723	2729	2735	2742	2748	1	1	2	3	3	4	4	5	6
.44	2754	2761	2767	2773	2780	2786	2793	2799	2805	2812	1	1	2	3	3	4	4	5	6
.45	2818	2825	2831	2838	2844	2851	2858	2864	2871	2877	1	1	2	3	3	4	5	5	6
.46	2884	2891	2897	2904	2911	2917	2924	2931	2938	2944	1	1	2	3	3	4	5	5	6
.47	2951	2958	2965	2972	2979	2985	2992	2999	3006	3013	1	1	2	3	3	4	5	5	6
.48	3020	3027	3034	3041	3048	3055	3062	3069	3076	3083	1	1	2	3	4	4	5	6	6
.49	3090	3097	3105	3112	3119	3126	3133	3141	3145	3155	1	1	2	3	4	4	5	6	6

LOGARITHM TABLES: Antilogarithms

	0	1	2	3	4	5	6	7	8	9	1	2	3	4	5	6	7	8	9
.50	3162	3170	3177	3184	3192	3199	3206	3214	3221	3228	1	1	2	3	4	4	5	6	7
.51	3236	3243	3251	3258	3266	3273	3281	3289	3296	3304	1	2	2	3	4	5	5	6	7
.52	3311	3319	3327	3334	3342	3350	3357	3365	3373	3381	1	2	2	3	4	5	5	6	7
.53	3388	3396	3404	3412	3420	3428	3436	3443	3451	3459	1	2	2	3	4	5	6	6	7
.54	3467	3475	3483	3491	3499	3508	3516	3524	3532	3540	1	2	2	3	4	5	6	6	7
.55	3548	3556	3565	3573	3581	3589	3597	3606	3614	3622	1	2	2	3	4	5	6	7	7
.56	3631	3639	3648	3656	3664	3673	3681	3690	3698	3707	1	2	3	3	4	5	6	7	8
.57	3715	3724	3733	3741	3750	3758	3767	3776	3784	3793	1	2	3	3	4	5	6	7	8
.58	3802	3811	3819	3828	3837	3846	3855	3864	3873	3882	1	2	3	4	4	5	6	7	8
.59	3890	3899	3908	3917	3926	3936	3945	3954	3963	3972	1	2	3	4	5	5	6	7	8
.60	3981	3990	3999	4009	4018	4027	4036	4046	4055	4064	1	2	3	4	5	6	6	7	8
.61	4074	4083	4093	4102	4111	4121	4130	4140	4150	4159	1	2	3	4	5	6	7	8	9
.62	4169	4178	4188	4198	4207	4217	4227	4236	4246	4256	1	2	3	4	5	6	7	8	9
.63	4266	4276	4285	4295	4305	4315	4325	4335	4345	4355	1	2	3	4	5	6	7	8	9
.64	4365	4375	4385	4395	4406	4416	4426	4436	4446	4457	1	2	3	4	5	6	7	8	9
.65	4467	4477	4487	4498	4508	4519	4529	4539	4550	4560	1	2	3	4	5	6	7	8	9
.66	4571	4581	4592	4603	4613	4624	4634	4645	4656	4667	1	2	3	4	5	6	7	9	10
.67	4677	4688	4699	4710	4721	4732	4742	4753	4764	4775	1	2	3	4	5	7	8	9	10
.68	4786	4797	4808	4819	4831	4842	4853	4864	4875	4887	1	2	3	4	6	7	8	9	10
.69	4898	4909	4920	4932	4943	4955	4966	4977	4989	5000	1	2	3	5	6	7	8	9	10
.70	5012	5023	5035	5047	5058	5070	5082	5093	5105	5117	1	2	4	5	6	7	8	9	11
.71	5129	5140	5152	5164	5176	5188	5200	5212	5224	5236	1	2	4	5	6	7	8	10	11
.72	5248	5260	5272	5284	5297	5309	5321	5333	5346	5358	1	2	4	5	6	7	9	10	11
.73	5370	5383	5395	5408	5420	5433	5445	5458	5470	5433	1	3	4	5	6	8	9	10	11
.74	5495	5508	5521	5534	5546	5559	5572	5585	5598	5610	1	3	4	5	6	8	9	10	12
.75	5623	5636	5649	5662	5675	5689	5702	5715	5728	5741	1	3	4	5	7	8	9	10	12
.76	5754	5768	5781	5794	5808	5821	5834	5848	5861	5875	1	3	4	5	7	8	9	11	12
.77	5888	5902	5916	5929	5943	5957	5970	5984	5998	6012	1	3	4	5	7	8	10	11	12
.78	6026	6039	6053	6067	6081	6095	6109	6124	6138	6152	1	3	4	6	7	8	10	11	13
.79	6166	6180	6194	6209	6223	6237	6252	6266	6281	6295	1	3	4	6	7	9	10	11	13
.80	6310	6324	6339	6353	6368	6383	6397	6412	6427	6442	1	3	4	6	7	9	10	12	13
.81	6457	6471	6486	6501	6516	6531	6546	6561	6577	6592	2	3	5	6	8	9	11	12	14
.82	6607	6622	6637	6653	6668	6683	6699	6714	6730	6745	2	3	5	6	8	9	11	12	14
.83	6761	6776	6792	6808	6823	6839	6855	6871	6887	6902	2	3	5	6	8	9	11	13	14
.84	6918	6934	6950	6966	6982	6998	7015	7031	7047	7063	2	3	5	6	8	10	11	13	15
.85	7079	7096	7112	7129	7145	7161	7178	7194	7211	7228	2	3	5	7	8	10	12	13	15
.86	7244	7261	7278	7295	7311	7328	7345	7362	7379	7396	2	3	5	7	8	10	12	13	15
.87	7413	7430	7447	7464	7482	7499	7516	7534	7551	7568	2	3	5	7	9	10	12	14	16
.88	7586	7603	7621	7638	7656	7674	7691	7709	7727	7745	2	4	5	7	9	11	12	14	16
.89	7762	7780	7798	7816	7834	7852	7870	7889	7907	7925	2	4	5	7	9	11	13	14	16
.90	7943	7962	7980	7998	8017	8035	8054	8072	8091	8110	2	4	6	7	9	11	13	15	17
.91	8128	8147	8166	8185	8204	8222	8241	8260	8279	8299	2	4	6	8	9	11	13	15	17
.92	8318	8337	8356	8375	8395	8414	8433	8453	8472	8492	2	4	6	8	10	12	14	15	17
.93	8511	8531	8551	8570	8590	8610	8630	8650	8670	8690	2	4	6	8	10	12	14	16	18
.94	8710	8730	8750	8770	8790	8810	8831	8851	8872	8892	2	4	6	8	10	12	14	16	18
.95	8913	8933	8954	8974	8995	9016	9036	9057	9078	9099	2	4	6	8	10	12	15	17	19
.96	9120	9141	9162	9183	9204	9226	9247	9268	9290	9311	2	4	6	8	11	13	15	17	19
.97	9333	9354	9376	9397	9419	9441	9462	9484	9506	9528	2	4	7	9	11	13	15	17	20
.98	9550	9572	9594	9616	9638	9661	9683	9705	9727	9750	2	4	7	9	11	13	16	18	20
.99	9772	9795	9817	9840	9863	9886	9908	9931	9954	9977	2	5	7	9	11	14	16	18	20

LOON (lün) A loon is any of four species of large water birds belonging to the family Gaviidae. Loons live only in the colder areas of the northern hemisphere. They are excellent swimmers. Loons are often called divers because they are able to dive as deep as 60 m [200 ft] to catch fish. Most loons spend the winters in or near the ocean. In the summer, they fly to northern inland lakes to breed. (*See* MIGRATION.) The female lays two or three eggs in a nest made of leaves and sticks. The nest is usually located near the edge of a body of fresh water. Both parents incubate the eggs until they hatch—about 30 days. Baby loons often ride on their parents' backs for several days or weeks before taking to the water themselves.

A common loon is about 90 cm [3 ft] long. Its wings and back are covered with black feathers that have white spots. The loon has a thick neck and a pointed beak. Its webbed feet are set so far back on its body that they are excellent for swimming but almost useless for walking on land. The legs and feet are also black. The black and white pattern of both male and female loons is most intense during the summer mating season. As winter approaches, this striking coloration fades to a somewhat duller gray without spots.

The common loon, or great northern diver, (*Gavia immer*) is found along the North American coasts from close to the United States and the Canadian border to as far north as the Arctic Circle. The red-throated loon (*Gavia stellata*) is the smallest of the loons and reaches a length of about 60 cm [2 ft]. Its neck is a chestnut red color during the summer. *See also* BIRD; GREBE.   A.J.C./L.L.S.

LOOSESTRIFE FAMILY The loosestrife (lü′ strīf′) family (family Lythraceae) includes about 50 species of dicotyledonous plants. They range from large trees to small annual plants. Members of the loosestrife family are distributed throughout the world. They all have opposite, simple leaves. (*See*

LEAF.) The flowers are of various colors, growing in clusters in the axils. (*See* INFLORESCENCE.) The flowers commonly called loosestrife are members of the primrose family and are not related to the loosestrife family. *See also* HENNA.   A.J.C./M.H.S.

LOUDSPEAKER (laud′ spē′ kər) A loudspeaker in a radio receiver or in a hi-fi sound system is a cone-shaped object that sends out sound waves. We hear these waves as music and speech. The cone is usually located inside the radio cabinet, or inside a wood or metal cabinet of its own. It works on the same principle that a telephone receiver does, but it is much larger and louder.

The cone, which is made of heavy molded paper, is made to vibrate by the attraction and repulsion of two magnetic fields. One magnetic field is produced in a moving coil, or motor, attached to the cone. The other magnetic field is a permanent one through which the coil moves. The moving coil carries the electric current caused by the incoming radio waves, or the electrical impulses from a record or tape. As the current changes back and forth, the strength of the magnet in the moving coil changes too, and the part of the cone called the diaphragm vibrates accordingly. The diaphragm moves the molecules of air near it and sets sound waves in motion.

Two other types of loudspeakers are the piezoelectric, or crystal, and the electrostatic, or condenser. In the piezoelectric type, a special crystal receives the electric impulses. It then causes the diaphragm to vibrate. In the electrostatic variety, the diaphragm is used as one electrode of a capacitor. It is suspended so that it vibrates freely. A fixed electrode is located very close to the diaphragm. Electric voltage between the two electrodes causes the diaphragm to vibrate.

A familiar type of loudspeaker is the horn speaker. It is used mostly for outdoor sound systems. The horn speaker consists of an extra-powerful diaphragm-type electrodynamic driver attached to a horn, or metal cone. Current from the signal is fed to a coil of wire. The wire is wrapped around a core that can be magnetized. The magnetism of the core varies in accordance with the received speech or music. This fluctuating magnetism attracts the magnetic diaphragm, which is a disk of thin iron. The disk vibrates and causes sound waves that are magnified by the metal horn in the same way a megaphone magnifies the human voice.   W.R.P./L.L.R.

LOVEBIRD (lov′ bərd) Lovebirds are any of nine species of small African parrots belonging to the genus *Agapornis*. Lovebirds are 10 to 15 cm [4 to 6 in] long and have bright green and yellow feathers. Many of them have a white ring around each eye. Like other parrots, lovebirds have short, curved bills (usually red in color) and short tails. When making a nest, the female of some species carries grass and twigs to the nesting site in her rump feathers. The female lays four to six eggs which hatch in about three weeks.

Lovebirds are so-called because they caress each other with their bills while courting and when perched and resting. They frequently imitate each other's actions, or join together in song. A pair of lovebirds stays together for life. *See also* BIRD; PARROT.

A.J.C./L.L.S.

LOWELL, PERCIVAL (1855–1916) Percival Lowell (lō′ əl) was an American astronomer. He was born in Boston, Massachusetts. He built the Lowell Observatory at Flagstaff, Arizona, in 1894 to study planets. Lowell was specially interested in Mars. He believed that the ''canals'' noticed by Schiaparelli had been built by intelligent beings.

Lowell predicted that there was another planet beyond Neptune. It was not until 14 years after he died that the planet Pluto was actually seen. It was first seen by Clyde Tombaugh at the Lowell Observatory.

C.M./D.G.F.

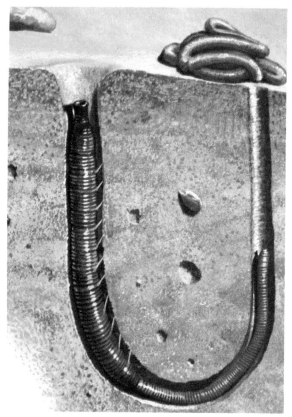

The lugworm (above) lives at the bottom of a U-shaped tunnel in the sand.

LUGWORM (ləg′ wərm′) The lugworm is any of several species of marine annelids belonging to the genus *Arenicola*. Lugworms have soft, segmented bodies and range in length from 10 to 40 cm [4 to 16 in]. The front end of the body is often dark red and is thicker than the yellowish red rear end. Lugworms obtain oxygen through 12 to 13 pairs of tiny gills located along the middle segments. The middle and front segments also have bristles.

Lugworms live in intertidal areas along the Atlantic coasts of North America and Europe. Some live in the Mediterranean Sea. At low tide, their burrows may be exposed. Lugworms dig U-shaped tunnels in the sand. Some of these burrows are as deep as 60 cm [2 ft]. Lugworms rarely leave their burrows, and constantly eat sand and decayed organic materials. The sand is ejected through the anus and left in coiled heaps near the burrow. Lugworms are sometimes called lobworms.

They are popular as a bait for deep-sea fishing. *See also* ANNELIDA.   A.J.C./C.S.H.

LUMBER

Lumber (ləm′ bər) is the wood of trees sawed into logs and beams and otherwise prepared for its many uses. About 75 percent of the lumber produced in the United States is used in buildings.

In the production of lumber, a great deal of sawdust and small pieces of wood is built up. However, this material is not wasted. Pulp mills treat the chips with chemicals, making wood pulp. Pulp is used to make paper, plastics, rayon, and many other products. Sawdust is used for fuel, insulation, and packing.

Types of lumber The two main types of lumber are softwood and hardwood. Hardwood comes from deciduous trees, those that lose their leaves in autumn, such as maples and oaks. Many important hardwoods grow in the dense rain forests of the tropics. Such tropical hardwoods include mahogany, teak, rosewood, and ebony. Hardwood is used basically for floors, furniture, paneling, and tools.

Conifers (mostly evergreen trees), such as pines, firs, and spruce, produce softwood lumber, used in construction and in making pulp. Plywood, used in construction, is made of several thin layers of wood glued together. Softwoods provide most of the world's lumber.

Raising the trees Foresters are the people who nurture the trees to maturity. A logger is a worker who cuts down trees, saws them into logs, and brings them to the mill. Sometimes the foresters decide upon block cutting, or clear cutting, in which all the trees in a certain region of the forest are cut down when they have reached the right age. Then the area is replanted. Sometimes nearly all the trees in a larger region of the forest are cut down, with a few "mother trees" left here and there to reseed the area of the forest naturally.

When foresters decide to replant the forest themselves, they use seedlings they have raised from seeds under ideal conditions in a forest nursery. They plant the seedlings in prepared ground when the seedlings are between three and five years old. The trees must be gradually thinned out as they grow to allow the remaining trees more room to grow to full size.

When trees have been felled, they are stripped of their branches and cut into short lengths.

Lumbering Logging is the first of three main branches in the lumber industry. Modern lumberjacks must be highly skilled in their work. Modern, large-scale lumbering operations require special mechanical equipment and technical knowledge.

The process of logging involves cutting down the trees, cutting them into logs, taking them out of the forest, and transporting them to the sawmills. The fallers, who cut down the trees, and the buckers, who cut the trunks into logs, use chain saws.

In cutting down a tree, the faller first makes an undercut, a wedge-shaped chunk taken out of the tree trunk with an ax or power saw. The faller makes the undercut on the side of the tree he wants to fall toward the ground. The cut is made close to the ground to avoid wasting valuable wood and leaving a high stump. After the saw has cut about three-fourths of the way through the tree trunk, the tree loses its balance and falls toward the side of the undercut.

The bucker trims the branches from the fallen trunk and cuts it into lengths of about 12 m [40 ft] or shorter.

Next comes the process of extraction, taking the lumber from where it has fallen to a central point called a landing. From there it is taken to the sawmills. If the landing lies near a road, trucks carry the logs to the mill. If it is on a railroad line, the logs are loaded onto flatcars for the trip. If the landing is near a stream or river, workers use chains to bind the logs into rafts that float to the mill. Sometimes barges carry logs.

From logs to lumber   In fairly large sawmills, logs are kept in a log pond until they go into the mill. The water protects the logs from insects, fungi, stain, and fire.

A moving conveyor chain carries the logs up a wooden chute into the mill. Water forced through overhead pipes give the logs a stinging bath. By the time the logs enter the mill, no sand, dirt, or small bits of metal remain on them that might dull the sharp saw blade.

A carriage carries the logs into the teeth of the headsaw. Each time the carriage goes past the saw, it slices off a board until the log is all cut. Moving belts carry the boards, called green lumber, to the edger, a set of smaller saws. These saws trim the rough edges from each board and make the sides straight and even. A set of saws called the trimmer makes the ends of the boards square. It also cuts the boards to the required lengths, and cuts off weak or bad spots.

Gang saws are used in some lumber mills, especially in Europe. In such mills, after the outer slabs of the logs are removed, the log moves into a set of straight-bladed saws. These saws cut the squared-up log into boards of the desired thickness in one operation.

The green lumber rides on a moving belt. Workers called graders test each board and decide its grade. They sort the boards according to size, quality, and type of wood. The boards are then stacked. They may be left for several months to dry.

Sometimes lumber is seasoned, which means removing excess moisture from the wood. More than half the weight of green lumber may be moisture. After seasoning, less than a tenth of its weight may come from moisture. A quick way of seasoning lumber is to put green lumber in dry kilns, in which the temperature of the air is gradually raised and the humidity lowered. Certain instruments tell how much moisture remains in the wood.

Logs may be used in other ways. They may be sliced very thinly to make veneer for manufacturing plywood or surfacing other pieces of lumber. Surface veneers, made from expensive hardwoods of attractive grain, are often glued to ordinary softwoods to make them look more attractive.

Shipping   Most mills ship lumber to wholesale dealers. The wholesalers sell to retail lumberyards, to factories, and to construction companies. Most long distance shipping is by rail or ship. Trucks make most of the short trips carrying lumber to all parts of the country.

J.J.A./F.W.S.

LUMEN (lü′ mən) A lumen is a unit used in light. It measures the amount of luminous flux given out by a source of light. (*See* FLUX.) The luminous flux is the amount of light that passes through a certain area. The brightness, or intensity, of a source of light is measured in units called candelas. (*See* CANDELA.) Imagine the source being at the center of a sphere, such as a ball. The source of light has an intensity of one candela. One lumen is the amount of light that falls on a certain portion of the sphere's surface. The area of this portion is the square of the sphere's radius. Technically, the cone from the center out to the area is called a unit solid angle or a steradian. The area of all the sphere's surface is 4π or 12.57 times the square of its radius. Therefore a source of intensity one candela gives out a flux of 12.57 lumens.   M.E./S.S.B.

LUMINESCENCE (lü′ mə nes′ əns) Luminescence is the glowing of an object and is caused by its atoms being excited by something besides heat. The atom can be excited by radiation, such as visible light or ultraviolet rays, or by electricity. The atoms absorb energy from the radiation or electricity. Then they give out energy in the form of visible light.

An atom is made of a number of electrons moving around a core called the nucleus. The electrons move around in orbits and each orbit has a different energy. Normally the electrons move in orbits that have the least energy. When an atom is excited, an electron absorbs the energy of the radiation or electricity. The electron now has extra energy and it moves into a higher orbit. Electrons need more energy to be in a higher orbit than a lower one. This is why, most of the time, electrons move in the lowest orbits. Usually the electron stays in the higher orbit for only a very short time. Then it gives off the energy and falls back to a lower orbit. This orbit may be the original one or it may be a different one. The amount of energy that it gives off is the difference in energies of the two orbits. The energy is released as a photon. A photon is a very small quantity of electromagnetic radiation. (*See* PHOTON.)

The difference in energy between the orbits can vary. If it is large, then X rays or ultraviolet rays are given out. If it is small, infrared rays or radio waves are given out. When the radiation is visible light, the process is called luminescence.

Sometimes the electron stays in its orbit long after it has been excited. The process of light emission is then called phophorescence. If the electron gives out light immediately after being excited, then it is called fluorescence. The luminous dial on some watches is an example of phosphorescence.

There are several methods of producing luminescence. Luminescence occurs when an electric current is passed through a gas. This happens in fluorescent lights. An electric current consists of a stream of electrons. The electrons collide with the atoms in the gas. These collisions cause the electrons in the atoms to jump into higher orbits. They then fall back again and the gas glows. The inside of a television screen contains a large number of phosphors. A stream of electrons is fired at them and they luminesce, forming a picture. Ultraviolet light can also cause luminescence. *See also* ATOM.   M.E./S.S.B.

LUNG (ləng) Lungs are the organs through which oxygen gets into the body of a human being or land animal. Carbon dioxide also comes out of the body through the lungs.

Animals that live in water usually have gills. These are feathery organs that spread out into the water. The lungs of land animals are really like gills turned inside out. They have to be moist because dry gases will not go through animal tissues. They are spongy so that there is a lot of moist surface for the gases to pass through.

Human beings have two lungs. They fill the chest (thoracic cavity) on either side of the heart. They are contained in a double slippery skin called the pleura. When we breathe in, our ribs and diaphragm make our chest expand. This makes our lungs expand so that air gets drawn in to fill them. The air comes in through the windpipe (trachea). This divides into two bronchi, with one half going to each lung. In the lung, the tubes divide again and again into thinner and thinner tubes (bronchioles). At the end of each bronchiole is a cluster of round sacs. These are called alveoli.

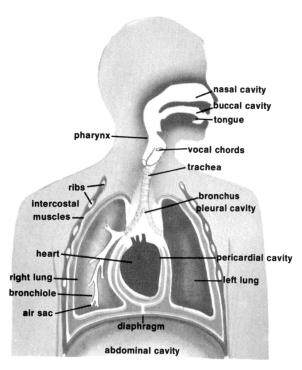

The organs that aid breathing are shown above.

When the diaphragm is lowered, air is drawn in through the mouth and nose. It passes down the trachea which branches into two bronchi. These divide inside the lungs, into bronchioles and air sacs. The air sacs are supplied with blood by a network of capillaries. In the alveoli, oxygen is first dissolved in a layer of moisture, and then taken into the red blood cells.

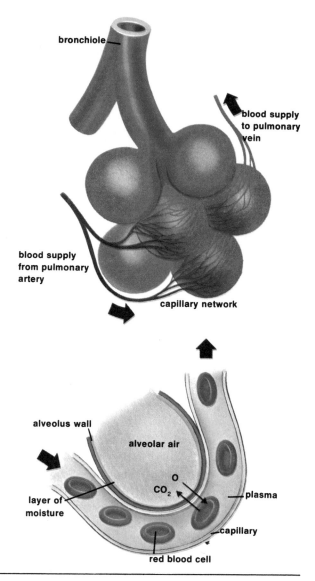

They have a rich supply of tiny blood vessels (capillaries) in their walls. It is here that the oxygen and carbon dioxide change places. Oxygen goes through the thin skin into the blood at the same time as carbon dioxide comes out. There may be 600 million alveoli in our lungs. They would give us about 232 sq m [2,500 square ft] of breathing surface.

In mammals, blood comes to the heart after going round the body and is then pumped to the lungs. The blood that has lost its oxygen and is full of carbon dioxide is immediately dealt with. Other kinds of animals have different systems. Birds have especially efficient lungs that can be completely emptied of air.

Reptiles are cold-blooded and do not need as much energy as birds and mammals. Their breathing system is less efficient. *See also* CAPILLARY; CARTILAGE; GILL; RESPIRATION; TRACHEA.   C.M./J.J.F.

LUNGFISH (ləng′ fish′) A lungfish is a freshwater fish that belongs to the class Osteichthyes. It is able to survive for long periods of time out of water because it can breathe air. When fish evolved, a saclike organ developed in the throat region of the lungfish. (*See* EVOLUTION.) This organ became the swim bladder, which is used to control the fish's buoyancy and gas content in the blood. (*See* SWIM BLADDER.) In lungfishes, this swim bladder developed into a primitive lung. (*See* LUNG.) Lungfishes can rise to the surface of water and gulp air to breathe into their lungs. Because of this ability, lungfishes are able to live in stagnant water with very little oxygen. Lungfishes do have gills, like other fishes, but these gills are poorly developed. (*See* GILL.) Scientists think that the lungfishes are similar to the ancient fishes that evolved into the air-breathing amphibians millions of years ago.

There are four species of lungfish in Africa, one species in South America, and one species in Australia. All six species live in hot regions. Often, a lake in which lungfishes are living will dry up during the dry season. To survive during this dry spell, the lungfishes will aestivate. This is a type of hibernation. (*See* HIBERNATION.) The fishes will lie in a muddy, cocoonlike covering with a breathing hole. This will prevent them for drying up. When heavy rains refill the lake, the lungfishes will emerge to swim and feed. *See also* AMPHIBIAN.   S.R.G./E.C.M.

Amphibianlike eggs of the Australian lungfish, or barramunda, are pictured above.

An African lungfish, *Protopterus*, is shown above.

LUPINE (lü′ pən) Lupine is the name of a group of plants in the pea family, genus *Lupinus*. About a hundred kinds of lupines grow in North America. Some contain poisonous alkaloids. The seeds of others can be eaten. Lupines bear long, showy, spike-shaped clusters of flowers. The flowers are (normally) blue, yellow, red, or white. They look like sweet peas. The leaves have several leaflets, arranged like the spokes of a wheel. Lupines are popular garden plants.

J.J.A./M.H.S.

Lupines belong to the pea family, Leguminosae. They bear long, showy spikes of flowers. The flowers at the bases of the spikes bloom first.

LUTETIUM (lü te′ shəm) Lutetium (Lu) is a silvery metallic element. It is one of the rare earth group of metals. (*See* RARE EARTH ELEMENT.) The atomic number of lutetium is 71 and its atomic weight is 174.97. Its melting point is 1,663°C [3,025°F] and it boils at 3,395°C [6,143°F]. Its relative density is 9.8.

Lutetium was discovered by the French

chemist Georges Urbain in 1907. He named it after the old name for Paris, Lutetia. It occurs in the mineral monazite and in other rare earth minerals. Its only use is as a catalyst in the chemical industry. (*See* CATALYST.)

M.E./J.R.W.

LYE (lī′) Lye is a strong alkali that is white and powdery. Its chemical name is sodium hydroxide (NaOH). Lye is also called caustic soda. It is made by the electrolysis of a solution of sodium chloride. Like other bases, lye neutralizes acids. (*See* BASE.)

Lye is often used in the home to clear clogged plumbing pipes. The base destroys wastes by eating into organic material. It is a very corrosive substance and must be used with great care. *See also* ALKALI.

J.J.A./J.M.

LYELL, SIR CHARLES (1797–1875) Sir Charles Lyell (lī′ əl) was a Scottish geologist. He was born at Kinnordy, Forfarshire, and studied at Oxford. He was called to the bar in 1827 but did not practice law. He became very interested in geology and toured Europe and America to study the rocks there.

Lyell supported the theories of James Hutton. In his book *The Principles of Geology* (1830–33) he put forward the view that the structure of the earth as we know it is the result of slow changes that are going on all the time. These changes, like erosion, happened in the past and are still going on today. He also studied evolution in connection with this process. He considered Darwin's theory of evolution in a paper called *The Geological Evidence of the Antiquity of Man.*

Lyell was knighted in 1848 and made a baronet in 1864. He is buried in Westminster Abbey. *See also* EVOLUTION; HUTTON, JAMES.

C.M./D.G.F.

LYMPH (limf′) Lymph is a watery fluid in our bodies. It passes through our body cells carrying dissolved substances with it. Lymph containing dissolved food, salts, and hormones passes out through the walls of blood vessels. It gradually gives up the things the cells need. At the same time, it picks up waste substances from the cells.

Lymph eventually drains into the lymphatic system and is returned to the bloodstream. It may carry white blood cells to a place where they are needed. The lymph that comes from the walls of the small intestine looks milky. This is because it contains droplets of fat. *See also* DIGESTION; LYMPHATIC SYSTEM.

C.M./J.J.F.

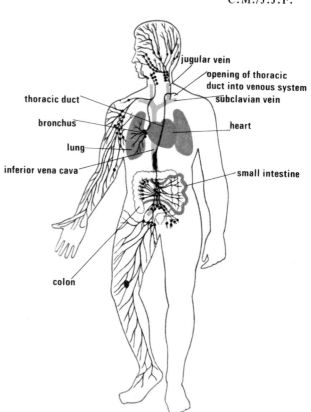

The lymphatic system (above) of the human body collects lymph from all the tissues and organs. It consists of a network of tubes which eventually drain into the veins of the neck. At points in the lymphatic system there are lymph nodes which contain blood cells which make antibodies.

LYMPHATIC SYSTEM (lym fat′ ik sis′ təm) The lymphatic system is a network of tubes that carry lymph away from body tissues. Frogs have lymph hearts to help the lymph along. We have no pump to keep the lymph moving. In humans, lymph moves from small vessels called lymph capillaries to larger ones called lymphatics by the pressure of muscles as we walk and move. Valves keep it going in the right direction. Eventually all the lymph pours into two large lymphatics called trunks. They empty the lymph into the subclavian veins, which run under the collarbone. Lymph flows very slowly. About 1.5l [3 pt] return to the bloodstream in one day.

Along the larger lymph vessels there are lumps called nodes. There are many of these in places like the armpits, neck, and groin. The lymph drains into them easily. But there is a kind of sieve at the other end that filters out germs and impurities. Therefore the lymph is cleaned as it passes back towards the bloodstream. The lymph nodes make many antibodies and special white blood cells that destroy harmful substances and germs. When people are sick, their lymph nodes may become swollen and painful. This is because the nodes are working hard to destroy the germs that are making the people sick. Tonsils contain the same kind of tissue as lymph nodes. *See also* ANTIBODY; BLOOD CELL; CIRCULATORY SYSTEM; GERM; GLAND; IMMUNITY; LYMPH.

C.M./J.J.F.

LYNX (lings) The lynx is a member of the cat family, Felidae. Most lynxes are powerfully built, and have stubby tails and long tufts of hair on their pointed ears.

The lynx is smaller than most other wild cats, such as leopards or mountain lions. Some lynxes may weigh 20 kg [45 lbs]. But most weigh from 6 to 11 kg [15 to 25 lbs]. Lynxes may be found in parts of North America and Europe.

Lynxes live in forests or in rocky, bushy places. They hunt mainly at night. They feed on snowshoe rabbits and other small animals. When their usual prey is scarce, lynxes may kill foxes and even deer. The female lynx bears from one to five babies in a litter.

The Canada lynx (*Lynx canadensis* or *Felis canadensis*) is the larger of two species that live in North America. The bobcat (*Lynx rufus* or *Felis rufus*), which is the smaller North American lynx, lives mainly in the United States.

The lynx's fur, which is a light gray or grayish brown, and spotted, is long and silky. The fur is valuable for use in scarves and jackets. *See also* BOBCAT.   J.J.A./J.J.M.

The lynx (above) is a member of the cat family.

LYRA (lī′ rə) Lyra is a small constellation between Cygnus and Hercules. It is visible in the mid-northern hemisphere from May to December.

Lyra contains the brilliant star Vega. Vega is the fifth brightest star, excluding the sun. Lyra also contains the Ring, or Annular Nebula. (*See* NEBULA.)

A meteor shower called the Lyriad radiates from just below Vega. The Lyriad occurs each year around April 21.

According to ancient mythology, Lyra represents a harp placed in the sky by the

Roman god Jupiter. *See also* CONSTELLATION; METEOR. J.M.C./C.R.

LYREBIRD (līr′ bərd′) The lyrebird is one of the most unusual of the perching birds. The two species of lyrebirds (*Menura superba* and *Menura alberti*) live in Australia. The lyrebird is about the size of a chicken. The lyrebird gets its name from the tail feathers of the male. These large and spreading feathers are arranged like a lyre, an ancient musical instrument. Two broad feathers curve upward with slender and delicate feathers in between. The lyrebird has brown plumage. Normally, the tail is carried low. But when it is raised, it is about 61 cm [2 ft] in length. The tail reaches full growth when the bird is about seven or eight years old. The male lyrebird displays its tail and sings to attract females during the mating season.

Apart from the tail, the two sexes are alike. Both have a strong, melodious song. They can imitate the songs of other birds as well as mechanical sounds.

The lyrebird can fly, but it uses its wings mainly for running and leaping. The lyrebird makes its nest on the ground. The females lay one egg in it. These nests are tightly woven and shaped like a dome. J.J.A./L.L.S.

MACAW (mə kȯ′) The macaw is a large parrot with a very long tail. It lives in Central and South America. Macaws usually live in forests.

The macaw has large, pointed wings and a short, hooked beak. The macaw's body is covered with brilliantly colored feathers of green, yellow, blue, and red depending on the species. The coloring is the same for both sexes. Macaws fly in pairs. They eat fruit, nuts, and seeds. These birds can be easily tamed and are sometimes kept as pets. However, their loud screams and the danger of their biting limit their popularity as pets.

J.J.A./L.L.S.

The male lyrebird has a tail of large, spreading feathers arranged in the shape of a lyre.

MACH (mäk′) Mach is a unit of measurement of the speed of objects which fly through the earth's atmosphere at velocities close to or above the speed of sound. The unit is named in honor of Ernst Mach (1838–1916), famous Austrian physicist and philosopher. Mach numbers are used because the speed of sound in the air is not always the same. The speed of sound depends upon the pressure (therefore altitude) and the temperature of the air. At sea level, at 0°C [32°F], sound travels at about 1,224 km/hr [765 mph]. But the speed of sound decreases at higher altitudes. At 13,000 m [40,000 ft], for example, sound normally travels at 1,062 km/hr [660 mph].

A Mach number is found by dividing the speed of an airplane by the speed of sound at the plane's altitude. For example, the Mach number of a plane flying at 1,200 km/hr [740 mph] at 13,000 m [40,000 ft] is 1,200 divided by 1,062, or Mach 1.13. A plane traveling exactly at sound speed, or sonic speed, is therefore flying at Mach 1.

Flight slower than Mach 1 is called subsonic flight. Speeds close to or at the speed of sound are called transonic. Flight faster than Mach 1 is called supersonic flight. When the Mach number is greater than 5, the speed is referred to as hypersonic.   W.R.P./J.VP.

MACHINE, SIMPLE

A machine (mə shēn′) is a device that can do work. The work may be lifting an object, or moving, crushing, or bending objects, and so on. Six different devices are generally recognized as simple machines. These are the lever, pulley, wheel and axel, inclined plane, screw, and wedge. By using these machines, people can perform tasks that they would not otherwise be able to do. For example, a pulley allows you to lift very heavy objects.

These simple machines can be put together to form other, more complicated, machines. For example, a wheelbarrow is a combination of a lever and a wheel and axle. Suppose that the wheelbarrow contains a heavy object. The back of the wheelbarrow can be lifted off the ground, despite the weight. This is because the barrow acts like a lever and allows you to lift heavy weights. A wheelbarrow also has a wheel and axle. This allows you to take the object from place to place.

Two terms often used with machines are effort and load. Effort is the force that you apply to the machine. Load is the force that the machine applies to the object. Without the machine, the effort would equal the load. With it, the effort is usually much less than the load. A pulley, for example, allows you to lift much heavier weights than you could without a pulley. In this example, the load is the weight of the object being lifted. The effort is the force needed to pull the rope attached to the pulley. The ratio of the load to the effort is called the mechanical advantage of the machine. The mechanical advantage is almost always greater than one. This is because the load is almost always greater than the effort. For example, suppose a machine allows you to move a load with half the effort that would be needed with no machine. Then the mechanical advantage is the ratio 2:1. (*See* IDEAL MECHANICAL ADVANTAGE.)

Machines allow you to move heavier loads than you could on your own. But this does not mean that you do less work. Work is closely related to energy. (*See* ENERGY.) The law of the conservation of energy says that the total energy in a system is constant. This means that the amount of energy in a system does not change unless energy is applied from outside. A simple machine does not create new energy, or work, by itself. For instance, a simple machine does a certain amount of work in moving a load. But you must put

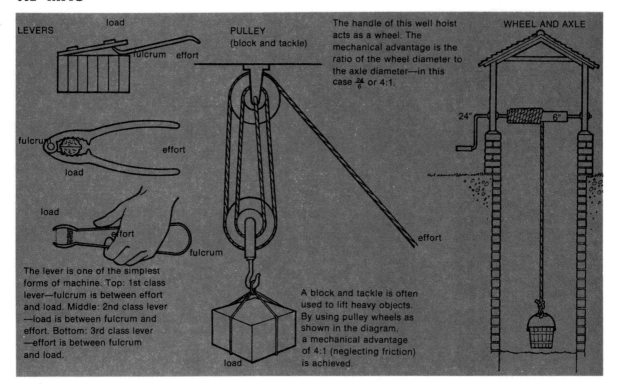

LEVERS

load

fulcrum   effort

PULLEY
(block and tackle)

The handle of this well hoist acts as a wheel. The mechanical advantage is the ratio of the wheel diameter to the axle diameter—in this case $\frac{24}{6}$ or 4:1.

WHEEL AND AXLE

fulcrum

effort

load

load

effort

fulcrum

The lever is one of the simplest forms of machine. Top: 1st class lever—fulcrum is between effort and load. Middle: 2nd class lever —load is between fulcrum and effort. Bottom: 3rd class lever —effort is between fulcrum and load.

effort

A block and tackle is often used to lift heavy objects. By using pulley wheels as shown in the diagram, a mechanical advantage of 4:1 (neglecting friction) is achieved.

load

24"   6"

work into the machine. The work you put in equals the work the machine puts out, less a small amount that is changed into heat in overcoming friction.

Work is equal to the force times the distance that the force moves. If you are lifting an object, work is its weight times the distance that it is raised. A simple machine allows you to use less force, but the force that you apply must move through a greater distance.

Suppose a pulley lifts a 10 kg [22 lb] object through a distance of 3 m [9.8 ft]. And suppose that the mechanical advantage of the pulley is 2:1. That means that only half as big a force as the weight of the object must be applied to the pulley. But you must pull the rope through twice the distance the object moves, or $2 \times 3 = 6$ meters. Thus the work done, which is force times distance, is the same as what it would take to lift the object directly.

The ratio of the distances moved by the effort and the load is called the velocity ratio. The effort almost always moves through a greater distance than the load. Therefore, for most machines, the velocity ratio is greater than one. In a perfect machine, the velocity ratio equals the mechanical advantage. Then, all the effort goes into moving the load. In a real machine, there is always some energy loss. The mechanical advantage becomes less than the velocity ratio. The ratio of these two is called the efficiency of the machine. A perfect machine has an efficiency of one. A real machine has an efficiency of less than one. This does not mean that energy is destroyed. Some of the effort does other work than moving the load. Most of the energy loss is due to friction. (*See* FRICTION.) Work has to be done to overcome the friction. This reduces the mechanical advantage and so reduces the efficiency.

Lever, wheel and axle, pulley The simplest kind of lever has a bar, pivoted about a support. The support is called a fulcrum. Effort is applied to one part of the bar. The bar pushes the load at another part. There is only a very small energy loss in a simple lever. The bar bends a little under the effort and this increases the amount of effort needed. Nevertheless, levers are very efficient machines.

There are three kinds of levers. A first class lever has the effort and the load on either side of the fulcrum. A crowbar and a seesaw are examples of first class levers. The mechanical advantage of this type of lever can be greater or less than 1:1. It depends on the distances of the load and the effort from the fulcrum. A second class lever has the load between the fulcrum and the effort. Its mechanical advantage is always greater than 1:1. An example is a nutcracker or a wheelbarrow. A third class lever has the effort between the load and the fulcrum. Its mechanical advantage is always less than 1:1. An example is a pair of sugar tongs.

In a wheel and axle, a rope is wound around an axle and attached to the load. The effort is applied to the edge of a large wheel attached to the axle. When it is turned once, the wheel moves through a large distance. But the load only moves a short distance since the axle is much smaller. The velocity ratio is the ratio of the diameters of the wheel and the axle. This is usually much greater than 1:1. Therefore the mechanical advantage is large and heavy loads can be lifted. Usually a handle is used instead of a wheel. The handle is pushed round in a circle. The wheel and axle system is used to draw water from wells.

The pulley is similar to a wheel and axle. Pulleys are used in cranes and hoists. They have one or more wheels with rope running in grooves around the outside of the wheels. If there is just one wheel, the effort equals the load. This kind of pulley allows the direction of the load to be altered. Instead of lifting a weight upward, you pull downward on the rope. This is much easier to do. Two or more wheels can be used, with the rope running from one wheel to another. In this kind of pulley, the effort is less than the load. These pulley systems are called a block and tackle.

Inclined plane, screw, wedge An example of an inclined plane is a board sloping from the back of a truck to the ground. To lift a heavy object from the ground to the truck is hard work. Instead, it can be pushed up the inclined plane. The gentler the slope, the less is the effort needed. Therefore the mechanical advantage is greater. But the object then has to be pushed further. This increases the velocity ratio. Much of the effort goes into overcoming friction between the object and the plane. This can be reduced by moving the object on rollers.

An example of a screw is the screw jack used to "jack up" automobiles. With a screw jack, a very heavy truck can be lifted by one person. But the handle of the jack has to be turned around many times. This means that the effort is being applied over a very large distance.

A wedge is similar to an inclined plane. Wedges are used, for example, to split wood. Force is applied to the thick end of the wedge. This drives the thin end of the wedge into the wood. The wood is forced apart and splits. An axe is a form of wedge.   M.E./R.W.L.

MACHINE TOOL (mə chēn′ tül) A machine tool is a nonportable, power-driven machine used to shape or finish metal. The metal to be shaped can be in sheet, bar, or block form, large or small. Different kinds of metal are often shaped by different types of machine tools. A machine tool is designed for automatic or semiautomatic operation. It performs repetitive tasks that would be very difficult or impossible to do by hand.

The most common use for machine tools is to make metal parts for machines. Almost all metal parts in an automobile or aircraft are made with the help of machine tools. The operator of a machine tool is called a machinist.

Some machine tools are small enough to be mounted on a workbench. Others are as

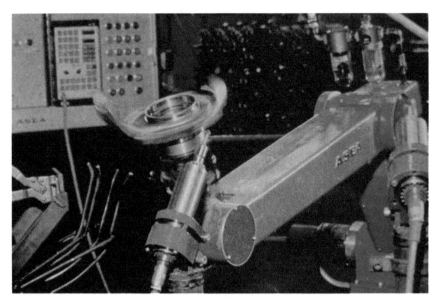

Many people think of robots as machines that look like human beings. However, most industrial robots do not look at all like humans.

large as a two-story house. Each machine tool is designed for a specific kind of work, from threading wood screws to forming aircraft wing frames.

Operations   The most common type of machine tool is the metalworking lathe. (*See* LATHE.) The piece of metal to be shaped—the work piece—is attached to spindles at each end and rotated at high speed. Various kinds of cutting tools can be attached to the lathe to produce the shaping desired. Gears, wheels, rods, and similar items can be manufactured on a lathe. Some lathes can perform more than one kind of shaping. Metal shaping on a lathe is called turning.

Another type of machine tool is the milling machine. This tool is most often used to cut or ''dress'' flat surfaces on solid metal. Its common form is a toothed wheel revolving at high speed, with the work piece being passed beneath it. Specialized milling tools are used to cut gear teeth, slots, and other shapes.

A drilling machine (or drill press) bores holes of various sizes with high accuracy. A stamping press might be used to cut electrical boxes from heavy sheet metal. A hammer press can be used to shape such metal parts as automobile bumpers and fenders. When sheet steel is to be shaped by a three-dimensional die, it is usually heated first to make it more pliable. (*See* DIE.)

Other work performed by machine tools includes planing, grinding, cutting, and polishing. A planing machine is used to give a piece of metal a flat surface. A grinding machine uses abrasives to do minor shaping—such as rounding sharp edges. A polishing machine uses very fine abrasives to give metal a bright, shiny finish. (*See* ABRASIVE.) Some cutting machines are designed to cut sheet metal, others to cut block or bar metal.

Most parts of machines are worked by several machine tools. For example, a blade for a circular saw is first stamped from sheet metal; one machine mills and another polishes the blade's surfaces; another machine cuts and shapes the teeth; another sharpens and sets the teeth; another drills the mounting hole in the center.

The cutting and shaping tools used on machine tools are made out of very hard steels (such as tungsten carbide). To lengthen a tool's useful life, lubricants are used to reduce the wear caused by friction. Oil and graphite are common. (*See* FRICTION.)

Working hard metals   The development of new, heat-resistant metals for use in space

Machine tools make it possible to manufacture components quickly and in large numbers. The large milling machine above is being used to shape the base of a marine bedplate. Below, on the right, are machines used to shape gears. The robotic system on the left can be programmed to perform many industrial tasks, such as handling materials, assembling electromechanical parts, and other high-precision work.

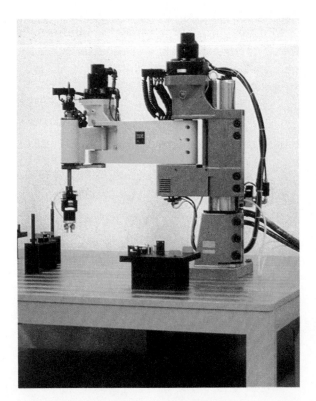

vehicles and jet aircraft has required the use of new types of machine tools. Some of these tools are as unusual as the metal alloys that they can shape. Some metals are best shaped in chemical etching baths (chemical machining). Others can be drilled by electrical sparks formed at the end of a shaped electrode (electrical discharge machining).

Laser beams have been developed to make small holes or precision cuts in metals. (*See* LASER.) Very hard metals can be worked by a process called ultrasonic machining. In this process, the cutting tool vibrates at a frequency far above that of audible sound; it cuts or grinds the metal into shape with the help of abrasives.

Industrial robots The use of computers to control machine tools and other machines has led to the development of the industrial robot. Simple robots are used for repetitive tasks like moving objects from one position to another. They are powered by air pressure or electric motors. Heavy-duty robots are usually powered by hydraulic pumps and motors. (*See* HYDRAULICS.)

Elaborate assembly lines of robots have been developed to perform a variety of work. A single computer can control the operations of several industrial robots.

Robots that perform the functions of machine tools usually have built-in, ''teachable'' computers. A machinist who is skilled at the work to be performed can instruct the robot through a control panel. The robot will ''remember'' the instructions and carry out its work in a consistent pattern, with consistent results.

Industrial robots are used mainly for tasks that are too strenuous, dangerous, hot, or difficult for humans to perform. Some of the newer machine tooling is safer with the help of a robot. *See also* COMPUTER. P.G.Z./G.D.B.

MACKEREL (mak' rəl) A mackerel is a saltwater fish that belongs to the family Scombridae. It is closely related to tuna. Mackerels swim in large schools, or groups, and are very fast-swimming.

There are seven species of mackerel found in the Atlantic and Pacific oceans. The Atlantic mackerel is a popular game and food fish. It grows to about 55 cm [22 in] in length. Most mackerel feed on surface plankton during the summer and on bottom-dwelling worms during the winter. The Atlantic mackerel, however, is a predator and feeds on small crustaceans, shrimp, and other small schooling fishes. *See also* BENTHOS; CRUSTACEAN; PLANKTON; TUNA.   S.R.G./E.C.M.

The common mackerel (above) is a streamlined fast swimmer. Mackerels are saltwater fish that swim in large schools, or groups. Seven species of mackerel are found in the Atlantic and Pacific oceans.

MAGMA (mag' mə) Magma is melted rock within the earth. When magma solidifies, it forms igneous rock. Geologists classify magma according to its silica content. (*See* SILICA.)

Magma forms beneath the earth's crust where the temperature and pressure are great enough to melt solid rock. The temperature of magma ranges from 482° to 1,371°C (900° to 2,500°F). It is expelled from the earth's interior through volcanoes and fissures. (*See* LAVA.) *See also* IGNEOUS ROCK.   J.M.C./W.R.S.

MAGNESIUM (mag nē' zē əm) Magnesium (Mg) is a soft, silvery metallic element. It is one of the alkaline earth group of metals. The atomic number of magnesium is 12 and its atomic weight is 24.312. Its melting point is 649°C [1,200°F] and it boils at 1,090°C [1,994°F]. The relative density of magnesium is 1.7.

The lava seen flowing in this picture is molten rock which has risen from deep underground. Molten rock beneath the surface is called magma.

Magnesium was isolated by the British chemist Sir Humphry Davy in 1808. (*See* DAVY, SIR HUMPHRY.) It is found in the minerals dolomite and magnesite. Most magnesium is obtained by the electrolysis of molten magnesium chloride. (*See* ELECTROLYSIS.)

Magnesium is a very reactive metal. It burns in air with a dazzling white flame. Because of this, magnesium is used in flares, flashbulbs in photography, and fireworks. Magnesium is used in a number of alloys. (*See* ALLOY.) Magnesium alloys are very light, yet they are also strong. This makes them very useful in aircraft parts, vehicles, and portable equipment. Magnesium alloys also resist corrosion. They are used to line water pipes and tanks. Magnesium has a number of important compounds. One of these is magnesium oxide. It is very resistant to high temperatures. It is used to line furnaces for melting metals. Two other important compounds are the sulfate and the hydroxide. Magesium hydroxide is used to relieve indigestion. When it is suspended in water, it is known as milk of magnesia. Magnesium sulfate is commonly known as Epsom salts. It is also used in medicine.

M.E./J.R.W.

MAGNETIC POLE (mag net′ ik pōl′) The magnetic poles of a magnet are those parts where magnetism seems to be concentrated. (*See* MAGNETISM.) A magnet has a north pole and a south pole. Since unlike poles attract each other, the north pole of one magnet attracts the south pole of another magnet. The north poles of two different magnets repel, or push each other away.

The earth acts like a huge magnet. The

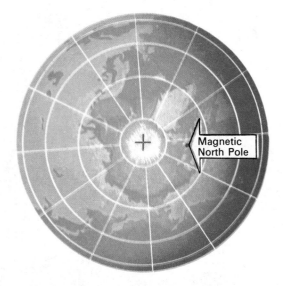

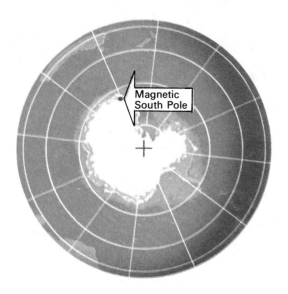

The magnetic north pole is near Prince of Wales Island in northern Canada. The magnetic south pole is in Wilkes Land in the Antarctic.

north pole of a suspended magnet tends to point to the north. The north pole of a magnetic compass is the end that points north. (*See* NAVIGATION.) Since unlike poles attract each other, this shows that the magnetic pole of the northern hemisphere really acts like the south pole of a magnet.

The magnetic pole of the northern hemisphere is called magnetic north. It is located about 1,600 km [1,000 mi] from the geographic north pole. The magnetic pole of the southern hemisphere, called magnetic south, is located about 2,400 km [1,500 mi] from the geographic south pole. The magnetic declination is the angle between the directions of the magnetic and geographic poles. The earth's magnetic poles change slightly from year to year. This causes a slight change in the angle of declination. J.M.C./J.T.

MAGNETIC STORM (mag net′ ik storm)
A magnetic storm is a disturbance in the magnetic field of the earth. Magnetic storms are caused by solar flares. Solar flares are violent eruptions on the sun's surface that seem to be associated with sunspot activity. Solar flares make the solar wind stronger. The solar wind is a stream of charged particles

(electrons and protons) moving at recorded speeds of more than 700 km [435 mi] per second. These particles enter and distort the earth's magnetic field.

Magnetic storms cause compass needles to work incorrectly. They also disturb radio transmissions. The concentration of charged particles near the poles during magnetic storms creates a magnificent display of colors in the sky. This sight is called an aurora borealis in the northern hemisphere. *See also* MAGNETISM; SOLAR WIND; SUNSPOT.

J.M.C./C.R.

MAGNETISM (mag′ nə tiz′ əm) Magnetism
has been known for thousands of years. Probably the earliest discovery of magnetism was lodestone, a mineral of iron oxide that is magnetic. About 800 B.C. the ancient Greeks discovered that pieces of lodestone attracted each other. Later the Chinese used lodestone to invent the compass.

The next discovery in magnetism came in 1600. In that year, the English scientist Sir William Gilbert suggested that the earth was a giant magnet. (*See* GILBERT, SIR WILLIAM.) This explained why magnets point to the North Pole. During the next few hundred years, more discoveries were made about magnetism. In this century, scientists discov-

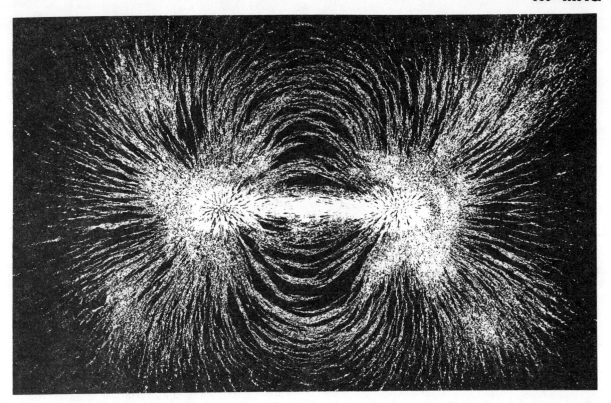

Magnetic lines of force radiate from magnet poles.

ered that the earth's magnetism (geomagnetic field) traps atomic particles in a region of the upper atmosphere, causing the zones of radiation known as the Van Allen belts.

Scientists now know that magnetism is caused by moving electrons. All matter is made up of atoms. Atoms have a central core called a nucleus. The nucleus is surrounded by a number of small particles called electrons (*See* ATOM.) These electrons have an electric charge. Whenever an electric charge moves, it becomes magnetic. The electrons move around the nucleus. Therefore, they are magnetic. Sometimes the magnetism of the different electrons in each atom cancels out. Then the material is nonmagnetic. In some materials, the magnetism of the different electrons combines. Each atom is then magnetic.

Magnets   Magnetism occurs most strongly in three metals: iron, cobalt, and nickel.

These metals can be used to make strong magnets. Iron is almost always used because it is the cheapest of the three metals. Usually magnets are made of steel, an alloy of iron. (*See* STEEL.) The two ends of a magnet are called the north pole and the south pole. The north pole points toward the North Pole of the earth when a magnet is suspended. Similarly, the south pole points towards the South Pole of the earth. If two like poles of a magnet are brought together, they repel each other. For example, the north poles of two magnets repel each other. Opposite poles attract each other.

Since magnets can affect each other without touching, they are said to have a magnetic field. (*See* FIELD.) The field extends outward from the poles of a magnet. If another magnet is placed in this field, it is attracted or repelled. The field around a magnet can be shown with iron filings. Iron filings are very small pieces of iron. A magnet is placed underneath a piece of cardboard. The iron filings are then scattered over the cardboard and gently sha-

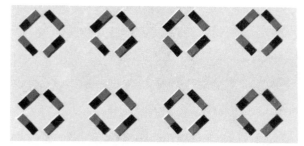
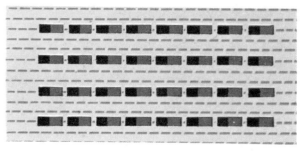

When a ferromagnetic metal such as iron is unmagnetized (left), the north and south poles of the domains attract each other, and as a whole cancel out the magnetism. When the metal is magnetized (right), the domains are arranged in lines, creating a powerful magnet.

ken about. The iron filings form lines called lines of force. These lines of force extend from each pole. As they move away from the poles, they spread out.

There are many ways to make a magnet. If a magnet is placed near a piece of iron, the iron becomes magnetized. A better way is to stroke a piece of iron with one end of a magnet. Magnets lose their magnetism if they are dropped, struck, or heated.

Iron can also be magnetized by using electricity. This is done by winding a coil of wire around a piece of iron. An electric current is passed through the wire. The current causes the iron to become magnetized. When the current stops, the iron loses its magnetism. This effect is used in large, powerful magnets called electromagnets. (*See* ELECTROMAGNETISM.)

Ferromagnetism There are different kinds of magnetism. For example, the metal bismuth is repelled by any magnetic field. This kind of magnetism is called diamagnetism. The most important kind of magnetism is ferromagnetism. Ferromagnets are strongly magnetic. The metals iron, cobalt, and nickel are the only ferromagnetic elements. Ferromagnetic materials are made up of many thousands of small magnets called domains. Normally, different domains point in different directions. Their magnetic fields cancel out and the material is not magnetic. When

the material is magnetized, the domains line up and point in the same direction. The magnetic fields of the domains combine to give a powerful magnetic field. When a magnet is demagnetized, the domains again point in different directions.

Some materials are very difficult to magnetize—for example, hard steel and some other alloys. Once they are magnetic, they are just as hard to demagnetize. Their magnetism is called permanent magnetism. Ordinary magnets are permanent magnets. Soft iron gains and loses magnetism easily. This is called temporary magnetism. Soft iron is used in certain electromagnets where the magnetism needs to be turned on and off.

M.E./R.W.L.

MAGNETITE (mag′ nə tit′) Magnetite is a black, metallic mineral. It is made of iron oxide (Fe_3O_4). Magnetite is an important iron ore. Some forms of magnetite, especially lodestone are powerful natural magnets.

Magnetite is found in scattered crystals (and sometimes in large masses) in igneous and metamorphic rocks. Grains of magnetite found in rocks give an indication of the positioning of the rocks when they were formed. The study of the magnetism in these grains provides information on early positions of the earth's magnetic field (paleomagnetism). This field of study is important in research into continental drift and magnetism of the earth. *See also* CONTINENTAL DRIFT; MAGNETISM.

J.J.A./R.H.

MAGNETO (mag nēt′ ō) A magneto is a device used to make a spark in internal-combustion engines. In an internal-combustion engine, a mixture of fuel and air is passed into a cylinder. The fuel is then ignited by a spark. The fuel reacts with the oxygen in the air and burns, producing hot gases. These hot gases push the piston along the cylinder. (*See* ENGINE.) Magnetos are used in motorcycles and most aircraft that have internal-combustion engines. They were also used in early automobiles but are not used in modern ones.

A magneto contains a magnet and two coils of wire wound round a piece of iron. One coil has only a few turns of wire. It is called the primary coil. The other has many turns and is called the secondary coil. Either the coil or the magnet is spun round while the other is kept still. This causes an electric current to flow in the primary coil. The current is said to be induced. (*See* INDUCTION.) The current is an alternating current. (*See* ALTERNATING CURRENT.) It builds up in one direction along the wire. Then it falls back to zero and builds up in the opposite direction. The primary coil is connected to a device called a contact-breaker. When the alternating current reaches a peak, the contact-breaker opens and stops the current from flowing. The current very quickly falls to zero. This induces an electric current in the secondary coil. The secondary coil has many more turns than the primary. This means that the induced voltage is very large. This large current is then passed to the spark plug to produce a spark.

Modern automobiles use a different system called battery/coil ignition. Magneto ignition is simpler and cheaper. But it does not work very well when the engine is being started. M.E./J.T.

MAGNETOMETER (mag′ ne täm′ ət ər) A magnetometer is an instrument that measures the strength of a magnetic field. Magnetometers are often used to detect variations in the earth's magnetic field. These variations help scientists find deposits of certain natural resources.

A simple magnetometer consists of a wire coil that makes an electric voltage when passed through a magnetic field. This voltage gives a measurement of the strength of the magnetic field. *See also* MAGNETISM.

J.M.C./J.T.

MAGNETRON *See* ELECTRONICS.

MAGNIFICATION (mag′ nə fə kā′ shən) Magnification is the enlargement of the view of an object or scene that an optical instrument gives. The magnification of an object can be described as the increase in apparent area of

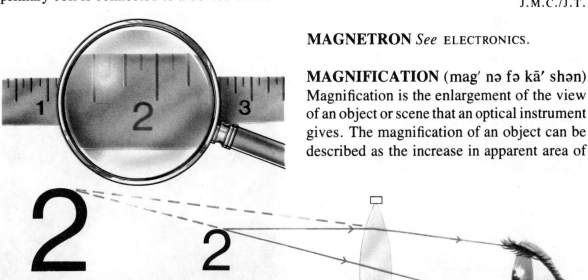

In this diagram, only rays from one point, and overall light refraction are shown. Actually, light is hitting the object from all points, and light rays are refracted at both surfaces of the lens.

the magnified object, or as the increase in the length of its sides. Magnifications are usually given as the increase in linear dimension (length of side). Therefore, a pair of binoculars with a magnification of X 10 makes an object appear 10 times nearer. That means that the length of its side appears to be 10 times larger than it is when seen by the naked eye. This is equal to an area magnification of 10^2, or 100 times. *See also* BINOCULARS; MICROSCOPE; TELESCOPE.   W.R.P./S.S.B.

MAGNITUDE (mag′ nə tüd′) Magnitude is a measurement of the brightness of a star as we see it from earth. In ancient times, stars visible to the unaided eye were classified into six magnitudes. The brightest stars in the sky were of first magnitude, while the faintest stars were of sixth magnitude.

The ancient system of magnitude has been slightly revised by modern astronomers. Today, a star of any magnitude is 2.5 times brighter than a star of the next magnitude. Thus a star whose magnitude is 1 is 2.5 times brighter than a star whose magnitude is 2. The modern magnitude scale extends both forward and backward to include stars that are very faint or extremely bright. Using large telescopes, astronomers can see some stars so faint that their magnitude is greater than 20. Some very bright stars have negative values of magnitude. The brightest star in the night sky, Sirius, has a magnitude of − 1.4. The sun has a magnitude of − 27.

Absolute magnitude measures the brightness of a star in comparison to the other stars.

	Apparent Magnitude	Absolute Magnitude
Sun	− 27.0	4.8
Full Moon	− 11.0	32.0
Sirius	− 1.4	1.3
Rigel	0.08	− 6.8

In order to do this, astronomers must determine how bright each star would be at the same distance away from the earth. Astronomers define this distance as 32.6 light years (10 parsecs). (*See* PARSEC.) For example, if the sun was 32.6 light years away from the earth, it would have a magnitude of 4.8. Hence, the sun has an absolute magnitude of 4.8. The absolute magnitude of Sirius is 1.3. *See also* LIGHT-YEAR; STAR.   J.M.C./C.R.

MAGNOLIA FAMILY The magnolia (mag nōl′ yə) family includes 12 genera (plural of genus) with 210 species of dicotyledonous flowering trees and shrubs. They have alternate, simple leaves, and large, single flowers growing at the ends of the branches. The flowers have many stamens and pistils, and usually 6 to 15 petals. The seeds hang by threads from conelike fruits.

The southern magnolia (*Magnolia grandiflora*) has large, white flowers, and grows throughout the southeastern United States. Big-leaf magnolia (*Magnolia macrophylla*) has the largest flowers and the largest undivided leaves of any native United States tree. The flowers are about 25 cm [10 in] across. The leaves measure about 75 cm [30 in] long by 25 cm [10 in] wide. *See also* TULIP TREE.
          A.J.C./M.H.S.

Magnolias are among the most primitive of flowering plants. The flowers of magnolias usually have 6 to 15 petals. The seeds hang by threads from conelike fruits at the center of the petals.

MAGPIE (mag′ pī′) The magpie is a bird belonging to the crow family. Magpies are found in North America, Mexico, Europe, and Asia. A magpie eats nearly all kinds of food. Its bulky nest has an opening in the side. For protection, the magpie often places its nest in thorny bushes. The female lays 5 to 10 grayish white, brown-spotted eggs. The magpie usually travels in groups. It is a noisy and aggressive bird. It can imitate various bird calls. Some magpies have been tamed and taught to speak simple syllables.

The black-billed magpie (*Pica pica*) lives in various sections of North America, Europe, and Asia. This species is black, with white feathers on the under parts and wing tops. The yellow-billed magpie (*Pica nuttalli*) lives only in California.   J.J.A./L.L.S.

MALACHITE (mal′ ə kīt′) Malachite is a bright green mineral from which copper is taken. Malachite is a copper carbonate which contains water. The mineral is frequently formed in layers that range in color from apple green to dark gray green. Sources of this mineral include Russia, Britain, Africa, Australia, and the United States (Arizona).

Malachite is used chiefly to make ornaments and mosaics. In ancient times, people made bracelets of malachite. It was believed that such bracelets gave protection against disease, lightning, and witchcraft.

J.J.A./R.H.

Malachite is used for ornaments and mosaics.

MALARIA (mə ler′ ē ə) Malaria is one of the most widespread, serious diseases in the world. It is caused by a parasite. (*See* PARASITE.) The parasitic animal is a one-celled protozoan that belongs to the family Plasmodiidae. There are four species that infect humans. There are over 15 species that infect other vertebrates. The protozoan lives in the red blood cells of the host animal. This weakens the host animal. It may kill it. Malaria is spread by mosquitoes. A mosquito bites an infected animal and sucks up some of the larvae of the protozoan. (*See* LARVA.) When the mosquito bites another animal, these larvae enter the blood of the new animal and infect it.

Malaria originally occurred throughout much of Africa, Malaya, Central America, Asia, South America, and the eastern half of the United States. However, people have been successful in eliminating malaria in many of these parts of the world. Africa, South America, and Southeast Asia still have widespread malaria. Malaria can be treated and cured with drugs, but the best way to fight it is to kill all the mosquitoes that spread the disease. The use of insecticides such as DDT has been successful in many places. The elimination of malaria in parts of Southeast Asia helped the United States Army defeat the Japanese during World War II. Until that time, nearly a fourth of all hospital patients during previous wars were sick with malaria. Malaria was a serious problem during the Vietnam War, too. *See also* BLOOD; DISEASE; PROTOZOA.   S.R.G./J.J.F.

MALLEABILITY (mal′ ē ə bil′ ət ē) Malleability is the capacity of a material to be hammered or rolled into thin sheets. Gold is one of the most malleable of metals. It can be beaten with great ease into extremely fine leaves so thin that it becomes translucent (permitting light to pass through). Other metals noted for their malleability are (in order of their malleability) silver, copper, aluminum, tin, zinc, and lead.

Some of the malleable metals, such as silver, aluminum, and copper, can also be drawn out into very fine wire without breaking. This property is known as ductility.

Any metal—even the almost unmalleable cast iron—becomes more malleable when it is heated. *See also* DUCTILITY.   J.J.A./J.T.

MALLOW FAMILY The mallow (mal′ ō) family includes about 75 genera (plural of genus) containing about 1,000 species of annual and perennial plants. They may be herbaceous plants, shrubs, or trees. Most are tropical. The leaves are alternate and may be lobed or divided with smooth or toothed margins. (*See* LEAF.) Frequently, tiny hairs cover the leaves, stems, and even the blossoms.

The flowers are usually large and brightly colored. They have five petals and five sepals. The flowers are usually perfect—that is, they contain both stamens and pistils. (*See* FLOWER.) Pollination is usually done by insects, though the flowers may fertilize themselves. (*See* POLLINATION.) Economically, the most important member of the mallow family is cotton. Other members include okra, hollyhock, and hibiscus. *See also* COTTON; DICOTYLEDON.   A.J.C./M.H.S.

The common mallow grows as a troublesome weed in many parts of Europe.

MAMBA (mäm′ bə) A mamba is a poisonous snake that belongs to the cobra family Elapidae. (*See* COBRA.) These snakes have fangs in the front of their mouths. The fangs have a groove down the back of them. The poisonous venom flows down this groove. The venom of a mamba can kill a person in 20 minutes. The black mamba, largest of all mambas, grows 4.2 m [14 ft] long. It lives on the ground. The smaller green mamba lives in trees. It is not as long as the black mamba. Mambas eat small mammals, birds, and lizards.   S.R.G./R.L.L.

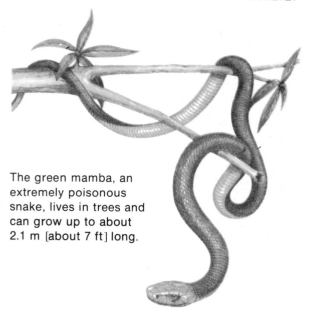

The green mamba, an extremely poisonous snake, lives in trees and can grow up to about 2.1 m [about 7 ft] long.

MAMMAL (mam′ əl) A mammal is a warm-blooded, vertebrate animal that belongs to the class Mammalia. (See VERTEBRATE; WARM-BLOODED ANIMAL.) Females have mammary glands which produce milk for the young. The bodies of most mammals are covered with hair. Some mammals, such as humans, have hair only on some parts of their bodies. Mammals are the most intelligent of all animals.

There are about 4,400 living species of mammals. They range in size from the 5 cm [2 in] long pygmy shrew to the 31 m [105 ft] long blue whale, the largest animal on earth.

Mammals evolved from reptiles about 180 million years ago. (See REPTILE.) The first mammals were very small—about the size of mice. As time went on, many more

The fox is a carnivorous mammal belonging to the dog family, Canidae. The red fox (above) hunts mainly at night.

species of mammals evolved. Many species have become extinct. (*See* MAMMOTH.)

One of the biggest differences between mammals and other animals is the way they reproduce. (*See* REPRODUCTION.) There are three different groups of mammals. Each group reproduces differently. The monotremes are the most primitive of all mammals. (*See* MONOTREME.) They lay eggs, but when the young hatch, they feed on their mother's milk like all mammals. The platypus is an example of a monotreme.

The marsupials give birth to their young before the babies have fully developed. (*See* MARSUPIAL.) The babies crawl into a pouch on their mother's belly. They feed on milk, stay warm and protected, and finish developing while in the pouch. The kangaroo and the opossom are examples of marsupials.

Most mammals alive today are placentals. The young develop completely while still inside the mother. The young are connected to the mother through the placenta, a group of tissues. (*See* PLACENTA.) In this way, the babies obtain food and oxygen without eating or breathing. The blood from the mother enters the babies through the umbilical cord. When this cord is cut, all that is left of it is the navel, or belly button. At this point, the young mammals must breathe and eat for themselves. They feed on their mother's milk for many weeks.

Mammals care for their young much longer than any other animal. Most animals—such as insects and turtles—never care for their young. They lay their eggs and leave. Most mammals care for their young until the young can protect themselves. Modern humans usually care for their young for at least 18 years. This extra protection helps the

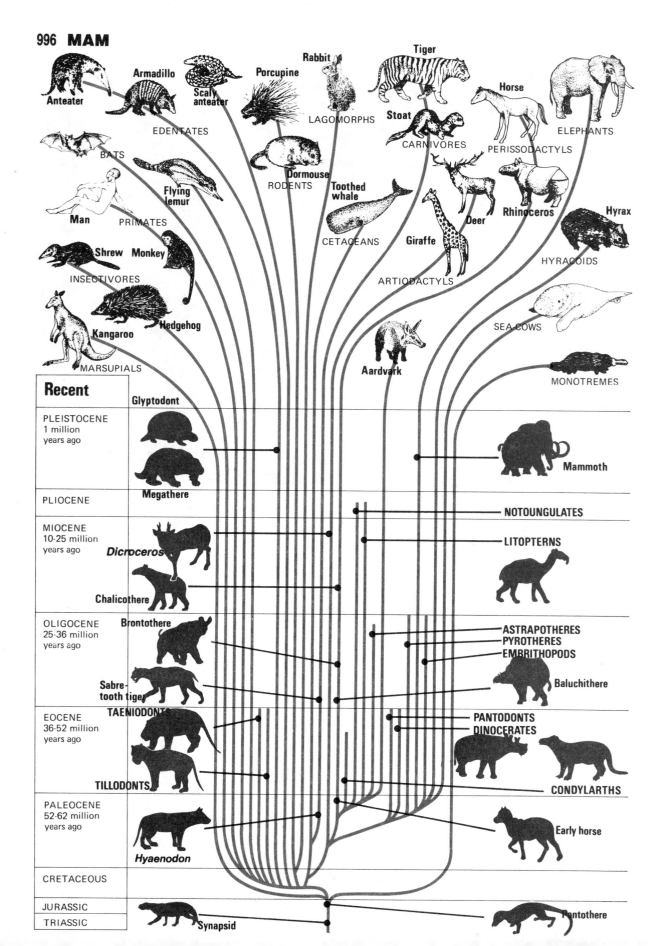

Anteater
Armadillo
Scaly anteater
EDENTATES
Porcupine
Rabbit
LAGOMORPHS
Tiger
Stoat
CARNIVORES
Horse
PERISSODACTYLS
ELEPHANTS
BATS
Flying lemur
RODENTS
Dormouse
Toothed whale
CETACEANS
Deer
Rhinoceros
Hyrax
Man
PRIMATES
Giraffe
ARTIODACTYLS
HYRACOIDS
Shrew
Monkey
INSECTIVORES
Kangaroo
Hedgehog
Aardvark
SEA-COWS
MARSUPIALS
MONOTREMES

Recent	Glyptodont
PLEISTOCENE 1 million years ago	
	Mammoth
PLIOCENE	Megathere
MIOCENE 10-25 million years ago	*Dicroceros*
	NOTOUNGULATES
	LITOPTERNS
	Chalicothere
OLIGOCENE 25-36 million years ago	Brontothere
	ASTRAPOTHERES PYROTHERES EMBRITHOPODS
	Sabre-tooth tiger
	Baluchithere
EOCENE 36-52 million years ago	TAENIODONTS
	PANTODONTS DINOCERATES
	TILLODONTS
	CONDYLARTHS
PALEOCENE 52-62 million years ago	*Hyaenodon*
	Early horse
CRETACEOUS	
JURASSIC	
TRIASSIC	Synapsid Pantothere

Facing left, a history diagram of mammals. The only mammals known from Jurassic and Cretaceous fossils (180 to 70 million years ago) were small creatures, rather like shrews. After the extinction of dinosaurs, these small mammals evolved rapidly and by Eocene times a great variety of mammals had appeared. As the diagram shows, many kinds of mammals eventually became extinct, but many others survived and are the mammals we know today. Right, a therapsid, a reptile that lived 230 million years ago and resembled a mammal in many of its body structures.

young mammals survive during the most dangerous period of their lives. Because more mammals survive, they do not have to give birth to as many young. Insects, fish, frogs, and turtles lay hundreds, sometimes millions, of eggs each year. Most mammals give birth to less than 10 young a year. Humans usually have only one baby at a time. *See also* ANIMAL KINGDOM; EVOLUTION; KANGAROO; PLATYPUS.   S.R.G./J.J.M.

MAMMOTH (mam′ əth) The woolly mammoth (*Mammuthus primigenius*) is an extinct member of the elephant family Elephantidae. Mammoths thrived during the Pleistocene epoch, which began about 2.5 million years ago. They probably became extinct at the end of the Ice Age, about 10,000 years ago.

Mammoths resembled the modern-day elephant. They varied in size, the smaller ones being about the size of a modern elephant, while some large mammoths measured 4.3 [14 ft] tall at the shoulder. The tusks of some mammoths were 4 m [13 ft] long.

Mammoths had fur and a thick layer of fat to protect them from the bitter cold of the Ice Age. The hair of the woolly mammoth was long, shaggy and covered the entire body.

Mammoths lived in Europe, Asia, and North America. They were hunted by prehistoric people, some of whom showed mammoths in cave drawings. In Siberia, several

mammoths were discovered perfectly preserved in ice. Mammoth fossils have also been found in Alaska, Texas, and New York. The reason for the extinction of mammoths is still unknown. *See also* PLEISTOCENE EPOCH.

J.M.C./J.J.M.

Mammoths existed in Pleistocene times. Many of these animals have been found whole in frozen soil and glaciers, allowing study of their soft parts and stomach contents. They are closely related to modern elephants.

MANATEE (man′ ə tē′) The manatee is a large water mammal. It is sometimes called the sea cow. The manatee belongs to the order Sirenia and is related to the dugong. It grows to about 4 m [14 ft] in length and weighs about 680 kg [1,500 lbs]. The manatee looks something like a walrus or seal. It has light to dark gray skin, with short, bristlelike hairs scattered over its body. The manatee has a set of short, paddle-shaped front legs and no hind legs. Its tail is rounded and is used for propulsion.

There are three species of manatee. The West Indian manatee lives in the Caribbean Sea and along the northeastern coast of South America. It is also found in the coastal waters of the southeastern part of the United States, particularly in the bays and rivers of Florida. The Amazon manatee lives in the Amazon and Orinoco Rivers of South America. The African manatee lives in the rivers and coastal waters of western Africa.

The manatee feeds on aquatic plants in fresh or salt water. It never leaves the water. The manatee can consume about 40 kg [100 lbs] of plants per day. Its upper lip is divided into halves which close like pliers on plants. Sometimes manatees are placed into waterways to get rid of aquatic plants that are choking the waterway.

The West Indian species has been heavily hunted for its flesh, hide, and oil. It is now classified as an endangered species.

W.R.P./J.J.M.

MANDRILL (man′ drel) The mandrill (*Papio sphinx*) is a large monkey. It lives in the forests of Cameroon and neighboring parts of western Africa. Mandrills look like baboons, having dark brown fur, long arms, and large canine teeth. The male mandrill is vividly colored. Its cheeks are blue, its nose is red, and its hind end is red and blue. The colors become more brilliant when the animal is excited. No satisfactory explanation of these colors has yet been put forward.

Like most monkeys, mandrills live in groups. They roam about on the ground. They feed mainly on fruits and other plants.

J.J.A./J.J.M.

The mandrill is a large baboon belonging to the Old World groups of monkeys.

MANGANESE (mang′ gə nēz′) Manganese (Mn) is a gray metallic element. Its atomic number is 25 and its atomic weight is 54.938. The melting point of manganese is 1,244°C [2,271°F] and it boils at 1,962°C [3,564°F]. The relative density of manganese is between 7.2 and 7.4.

Manganese was discovered in 1774 by the Swiss chemist Johann Gahn. Most manganese is obtained from the mineral pyrolusite. This mineral contains manganese dioxide. Pyrolusite is mixed with a reactive metal, such as powdered aluminum, and heated. This metal combines with the oxygen in manganese dioxide. This sets the manganese free.

Manganese is important in alloys. (*See* ALLOY.) It is added to steel to harden it and to make it more resistant to wear. It is also added to other alloys, such as bronze.

Manganese forms a number of important compounds. Manganese dioxide is used in industry as a catalyst and an oxidizing agent. (*See* CATALYST; OXIDATION AND REDUC-

TION.) Manganese salts are used in ceramics and dyes. Potassium permanganate is a purple, crystalline solid. It is a powerful oxidizing agent and is used as a disinfectant.

M.E./J.R.W.

MANGO (mang′ gō) The mango (*Mangifera indica*) is a large, evergreen tree that thrives in tropical and subtropical areas. It often reaches a height of 18 m [60 ft]. The alternate, narrow leaves are about 30 cm [1 ft] long, and are simple and leathery. The pink or white flowers grow in clusters at the ends of small branches. (*See* INFLORESCENCE.)

The mango fruit is usually about the size of an apple, but it may grow to weigh more than 2 kg [4.4 lb]. It is usually red or yellow with black spots. It has a soft, juicy pulp which is very tasty and is a good source of vitamins A, C, and D. (*See* VITAMIN.)

A.J.C./F.W.S.

MANGROVE (man′ grōv′) The mangrove is any of several dicotyledonous trees that grow well in salty ocean swamps and lagoons near the coasts. A mangrove tree produces hundreds of adventitious roots from the branches. (*See* ROOT.) These aerial roots keep the leafy part of the tree above the water, even at high tide. The roots tend to catch silt and other debris. This causes the buildup of mud and earth near the tree. Since the roots need to be exposed to salt water, however, the mangrove may kill itself as it reclaims land from the sea.

The mangrove seed germinates while it is still on the tree. (*See* GERMINATION.) The seed produces a root that is about 30 cm [1 ft] long. If this root touches the collected silt and mud near the tree, it begins to grow into a new tree—often while still attached to the parent tree. At other times, when the fruit falls off the tree, the root acts like the keel of a boat to keep the seed upright as it floats in the water. (*See* DISPERSION OF PLANTS.) If a floating seed germinates in the mud, its roots develop air tubes which rise above the water to get oxygen. (*See* PNEUMATOPHORE.)

The most common mangrove is the red mangrove (*Rhizophora mangle*). This tree grows from Florida to South America in protected ocean areas along the coasts. It reaches a height of 9 m [30 ft]. It has opposite, leathery leaves that sometimes reach a length of 15 cm [6 in]. The red mangrove has pale yellow flowers. The bark yields the chemical tannin which is used in tanning leathers.

A.J.C./M.H.S.

Above, aerial roots of mangroves project above water in a swampy region.

MANOMETER (mə näm′ ət ər) A manometer is an instrument used to measure the pressure of gas. There are several types of manometers. The most common type consists of a U-shaped tube with both ends open. The tube contains a liquid, often mercury, that fills the bottom of the U and rises a short distance in each arm. To measure the pressure of a gas, the open end of one arm is attached to a hose or pipe containing the gas. The other end of the U remains open to the atmosphere. In this way, the liquid in the tube is exposed to the pressure of the gas in one arm, and the pressure of the atmosphere in the other arm.

If the pressure of the gas is higher than the pressure of the atmosphere, the liquid rises in the arm of the tube exposed to the air. The difference between the heights of the liquid in both arms is measured to determine the pressure of this amount of liquid. The sum of this pressure and the atmospheric pressure is the pressure of the gas.

Gas pressure is often measured in units of the height of the liquid in the manometer. For example, gas pressure is often expressed as centimeters of mercury. Normal atmospheric pressure is 76 cm.

In some manometers, the air is removed from one end of the tube and that end is sealed. This eliminates difficulties caused by changes in atmospheric pressure. The difference between the levels of liquid in the arms shows the pressure of the gas. This type of manometer is usually called a vacuum gauge or pressure gauge.

Some manometers work on the principle of a spring attached to an indicator. The indicator moves in front of a graduated scale that gives direct pressure readings. This type is called the sphygmomanometer. Doctors use it to measure people's blood pressure. *See also* BAROMETER.   W.R.P./J.T.

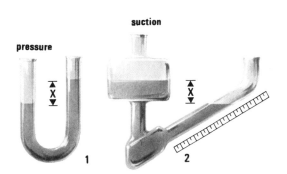

1. An ordinary U-tube manometer. When no pressure is applied, the liquid levels in the two "arms" are the same. When a small gas pressure is applied in one arm, the liquid level will rise in the other. The pressure can then be measured by the difference in level, shown here as X. 2. Another manometer, in which one arm of the U-tube is tilted at an angle to the other, which is enlarged. A small difference in pressure, shown here as negative pressure, X, will cause a large difference in pressure in the angled tube.

MANTIS (mant′ əs) The mantises are long slender insects in the order Mantodea. They are commonly called praying mantises. This name refers to their habit of lifting the front legs toward the head, as if in prayer. The mantis takes this position when hunting. When an insect comes within range, the mantis's front legs shoot out at great speed. The prey is trapped in the mantis's viselike grip. Mantises not only feed on other insects, but on other mantises as well. If a female mantis is hungry, she may eat her own mate.

Above, a mantis.

A mantis and its prey.

Mantises are usually found in warm countries, though the common European mantis lives in the northern regions of the United States. Depending on the species, a full-grown mantis ranges from about 5 to 13 cm [2 to 5 in] in length. The insect's wings are short and broad, folded flat on the back. The mantis blends in color with the plants on which it stays. (*See* CAMOUFLAGE.)

Each female mantis lays its eggs in a mass. The mass is glued to trees and shrubs by a sticky brown substance from the female's body, which hardens as it dries. The young hatch in the spring. Mantises are helpful to human beings. The insects often eat other insects that are harmful to people.

J.J.A./J.E.R.

MANTLE (mant′ əl) The mantel is the portion of the earth between the crust and the core. It is located about 30 km [19 mi] beneath the earth's surface. The 2,900 km [1,800 mi] thick mantle is composed of dense rocks. These rocks are made up of minerals containing aluminum, iron, magnesium, oxygen, and silicon. The minerals are sometimes brought to the earth's surface through volcanoes.

The boundary between the earth's crust and the mantle is called the Mohorovicic Discontinuity, or Moho. On land, the Moho is about 32 km [20 mi] beneath the surface, but under the oceans it is only about 8 km [5 mi] down. (*See* MOHO.)

The earth's mantle is under great pressure and temperature. The upper mantle near the Moho has a temperature of about 870°C [1,600°F]. The lower mantle near the earth's outer core has a temperature of about 2,200°C [4,000°F].

For years, geologists have wanted to drill a hole through the earth's crust to the mantle. In the 1960s this project was started, but it was abandoned by the government in 1964 because of other matters taking greater priority. Scientists have learned from seismology (the study of earthquakes) that in the upper mantle rocks are plastic, not rigid. This upper zone of the mantle is called the asthenosphere. Scientists have suggested that the movement of the continents is caused to some degree by the mantle. (*See* CONTINENTAL DRIFT.) Some geologists believe that some rocks in Cyprus may be mantle rocks, formed when Cyprus was forced up by the pressure of the African land mass pushing against Europe. *See also* EARTH; PLATE TECTONICS.

J.M.C./W.R.S.

MAP AND MAPPING A map (map) is a representation of part or all of the earth on a flat surface or globe. There are many different types of maps, most of which can be divided into two main groups: reference maps and special maps.

Reference maps Reference maps portray cities, countries, continents, and bodies of water. A road map is a reference map used by travelers. Other types of transportation maps are used by police and the military. A book of reference maps is called an atlas.

Special maps Special maps emphasize a certain characteristic or feature of an area. For example, a physical map emphasizes the landscape of an area, either by color or as a three-dimensional model. (*See* TOPOGRAPHY.) A population map shows different population densities by degrees of shading. A weather map represents the weather systems affecting a given area on a map.

Scale Maps are drawn to scale. This means that a given distance on a map equals a larger distance on the earth's surface. A map must be drawn to scale to be accurate.

Some maps use an equality to explain the scale, like 1 cm = 14 km. This equality means that 1 cm on the map is equal to 14 km on the earth's surface. This type of scale may be confusing to somebody who does not under-

Surveyors use instruments such as this theodolite to make accurate measurements. Distances and directions are measured to relate different places on the earth's surface to each other.

stand the system of units being used. This potential problem is overcome by using a ratio or fraction scale, like 1:60,000 or 1/60,000. The fraction or ratio means that one unit on the map is equal to 60,000 units on the earth's surface. This method of scale is accurate regardless of the system of units used.

Map symbols Map symbols make a map easier to read. Sometimes these symbols look like what they are representing. For example, a symbol shaped like a cow may represent an area of dairy farming on an agricultural map. A dot is often used to represent a city. The size of the dot may indicate the population of the city. Most maps have legends or keys that explain the symbols.

Lines that link places of equal value are called isolines. Contours are isolines that link places of equal altitude. Isotherms link places of equal temperature on a weather map. (*See* ISOBAR AND ISOTHERM.)

Color Color is another aid in reading a map. Countries or states are often shown in different colors to give contrast. For example, a map of North America may show Canada in green, the United States in yellow, and Mexico in red. These colors make the countries easy to distinguish.

Color is also used to represent the altitude of a land. Shading is sometimes used to show differences in rainfall in a given area, or to portray population densities.

Finding locations on a map Latitude and longitude describe locations on a map. Lines of latitude, called parallels, include the equator and the circles parallel to it. Lines of

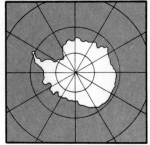

Azimuthal projections are made by supposing a light source to be at the center of a globe that is touching a piece of paper at one point. Here, the globe touches the paper at the South Pole. But the distortion made by this projection means that distances are increasingly "stretched" farther away from the South Pole.

Conic projections are made onto a cone of paper. The distances are distorted. The least distortion occurs at the Standard Parallel, the line where the cone touches the globe. Here, a conic projection of the North Pole.

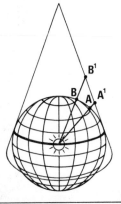

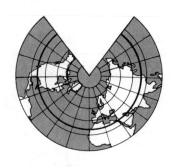

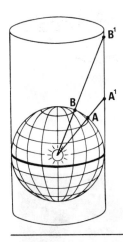

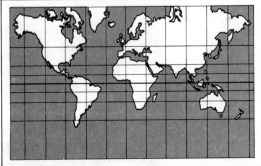

A cylindrical projection is made as if a light at the center of the globe is casting a shadow onto a cylinder of paper wrapped around the globe. Here the cylinder touches the globe along the equator. The lines of latitude (A and B) get farther apart (A¹ and B¹) nearer the poles.

The only map projection that does not make distortions is the globe (top left) because this is a true representation of the earth. However, only part of the earth can be seen at one time. An interrupted projection (top right) is made by peeling off the surface of the globe like an orange. But it is not very useful as a map. A sinusoidal projection (bottom left) shows the whole world, but the areas at top, bottom, right and left are distorted. A Mercator projection (bottom right) shows areas near the poles larger than they actually are.

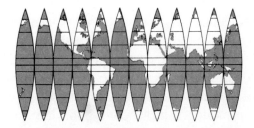

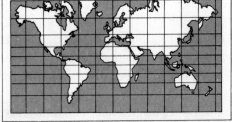

longitude, called meridians, run north and south at right angles to the equator. Knowing the latitude and longitude of a certain place makes it easier to locate.

Some maps provide an alphabetical index of places on the map. In the index, each place is followed by a number and a letter. The number corresponds to numbers which run along the top and bottom of the map. The letter corresponds to letters which run along the sides of the map. On a map of the United States, New York City could be located by looking in the index. If the index says 7H for New York City, then New York City lies where a line drawn from 7 meets a line drawn from H.

The making of a map   The making of a map involves the work of many specially trained scientists. These scientists make many observations of the area to be mapped. The area is photographed, and measurements of distance, direction, and elevation are taken. Aerial photographs are studied and interpreted.

Many scientific instruments are used to make a map. A theodolite measures horizontal and vertical angles over a long distance. By using this device, map makers can determine distances from one point to another. A tellurometer determines distances by measuring the time it takes radio waves to travel between two points. Another instrument determines distance by measuring the speed of light waves.

A level is a device used to measure elevation. A clinometer is used to measure the angle of elevation between two points.

Aerial photography has come into wide use since World War II. Aerial photographs show tremendous detail and help in the mapping of rugged mountain areas. Photogrammetry is the science of making measurements from air photographs.

When all the observations, photographs, and surveying have been completed and analyzed, a cartographer (mapmaker) or-

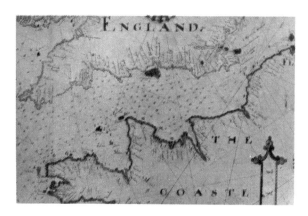
A chart of the English Channel, drawn in 1596.

Surveyors using a theodolite to map a desert area in Oman.

Aerial photographs are often used to make maps. Here, individual houses and fields can be seen clearly, along with roads and a river.

ganizes the data into a map plan. From this plan, the cartographer incorporates the data into an accurate, easy-to-read map.

Map projections The only map that is completely accurate is a global map. Globes show locations, shapes, and distances correctly. Unfortunately, a globe is clumsy to carry around, and only one part of a globe can be observed at a time.

Therefore, cartographers have devised map projections, which are flat maps, projected from a globe, made as accurate as possible.

There are several types of map projections. As azimuthal projection projects the surface of a globe on a flat surface that touches the globe at only one point. This type of projection results in distortion of distance.

A cylindrical projection projects the earth's surface on a piece of paper wrapped around a globe. This results in a map where all the meridians are at right angles to the parallels. On a cylindrical projection, the extreme north and south polar areas have distorted distances.

A conical projection projects an area of the earth's surface on a cone of paper placed over the globe. Again, some distortion of distance occurs.

Some projections, called conventional projections, are variations of a global map of the world. Conventional projections include sinusoidal projections, interupted projections, and mercator projections. *See also* EARTH; GEODESY; LATITUDE AND LONGITUDE.   J.M.C./W.R.S.

MAPLE FAMILY The maple (mā' pəl) family includes about 150 species of trees growing in northern temperate zones throughout the world. There are 13 species native to the United States. The large, flat leaves are opposite, and are usually divided into three to seven lobes. (*See* LEAF.) The flowers are small and greenish, with four or five petals. The seeds usually grow in pairs and are enclosed in dry, flat, winglike fruits called keys. (*See* DISPERSION OF PLANTS.)

The most important member of the maple family in North America is the rock maple (*Acer saccharum*). It is also called the sugar maple or the hard maple. Its wood is light, reddish brown, and is very hard and strong, making it valuable as lumber. The rock maple grows to a height of about 41 m [135 ft]. It has dark green leaves which change to brilliant red, yellow, and orange in the fall. The rock maple yields a sugary sap which is processed into maple syrup, maple sugar, and other products.

The maple leaf is the national emblem of Canada, and it appears on the Canadian flag. Other important members of the maple family include the silver maple, the Japanese maple, the sycamore, and the box elder.

A.J.C./M.H.S.

MARBLE (mär' bəl) Marble is a type of hard limestone that takes a high polish. It is formed from limestone that has been

Marble is a form of hard limestone. The coloring in marble is caused by the presence of other minerals or small amounts of staining matter mixed in with the marble stone. Pure marble is white.

metamorphosed (changed) by the tremendous heat and pressure beneath the earth's surface. The limestone becomes a hard, crystalline rock without cavities and holes. The crystals that make up pure marble are of the minerals calcite and dolomite. Pure marble is snow white. Colored and banded marble contain various impurities.

Marble was used in ancient times for statues and fine buildings. The quarries of Carrara, Italy, are known for their high-quality marble. Famous sculptors, like Michelangelo and Leonardo da Vinci, used this marble for many of their works. In the United States the largest marble quarry is located in Vermont. *See also* LIMESTONE; METAMORPHIC ROCK.   J.M.C./W.R.S.

MARCONI, GUGLIELMO (1874–1937)

Guglielmo Marconi (mär kō′ nē) was an Italian electrical engineer. He was born at Bologna. He heard that Heinrich Hertz had discovered radio waves in 1887. Marconi had the idea that these waves could be used to carry messages. At that time, messages were already being sent in Morse code using electric wires. After working on the problem for some time, Marconi produced an electric bell that could be run from 9.3m [30 ft] away. The bell was switched on by an electrical pulse that was carried across 30 feet by radio waves.

By 1895 Marconi had developed equipment good enough to transmit pulses as far as a mile. But the Italian government was not interested in his work. Marconi decided to try his luck in England. The British government was very helpful and granted him a patent. With this patent Marconi was able to start the Marconi Company in 1897. (*See* RADIO.) Two years later he transmitted a radio signal across the English channel. On December 12, 1901, the letter S was sent in Morse code across the Atlantic Ocean. It came from Poldhu, Cornwall, to Marconi

Guglielmo Marconi devoted his life to radio communications. In 1896 the British government granted him the first radio patent, which was based in part on the theory that the distance of radio communication increases rapidly as the height of the antenna is increased. In 1901 Marconi sent a message across the Atlantic Ocean.

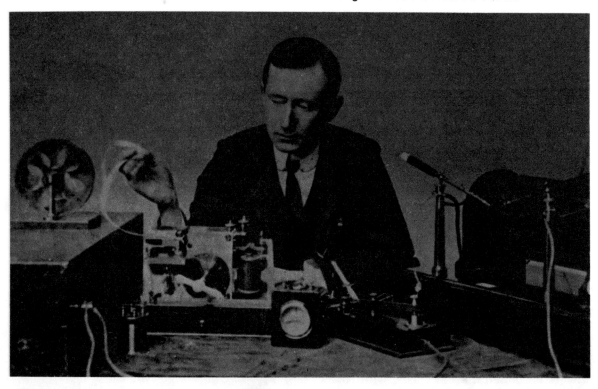

who was at Signal Hill, St. John's, Newfoundland. Marconi went on experimenting and improving radio transmission all his life. He was awarded the Nobel Prize for Physics in 1909.   C.M./D.G.F.

MARIJUANA (mar′ ə wän′ ə) Marijuana is a drug derived from the leaves and flowers of the hemp plant (*Cannabis sativa*). The active ingredient in marijuana is tetrahydrocannabinol (THC). Since the amount of THC varies from plant to plant, the strength of marijuana also varies. Marijuana is usually rolled into a cigarette and smoked, though it may be cooked into foods and eaten. Marijuana cigarettes are commonly called joints or reefers. The effects of smoking marijuana may last for as long as five hours, while eating marijuana may produce effects for 12 hours.

The effects of marijuana vary and depend on the strength of the marijuana, the amount used, the setting in which it is used, and the experience of the user. There is usually a feeling of euphoria (happiness and well-being). When used in large amounts, there may be some distortion of vision, time, and space. Minutes may seem like hours, and short distances may seem to be much longer. Since this drug may intensify emotions and sensations, a person who is unhappy or depressed may become even more so after its use. Marijuana causes several physical effects such as reddening of the eyes, increased heart rate, decreased blood pressure, and increased appetite.

Marijuana has been used in Oriental cultures for thousands of years. It is now used by people throughout the world. There has been much public and scientific controversy about marijuana. No proof exists that, as some believe, marijuana use leads to the use of hard drugs such as heroin. (*See* NARCOTIC.) There is also no proof that its uses causes antisocial or violent behavior. Smoking marijuana can be as harmful as smoking tobacco, however.

And usage can effect sperm production, fertility, and menstrual regularity. Frequent usage of marijuana has not been found to cause physical addiction. (*See* ADDICTION.)

In 1937, the United States outlawed the possession, use, or sale of marijuana. Since relatively few people used the drug, the issue remained largely dormant for about 30 years. In the 1960s, however, the use of marijuana increased dramatically, and the controversy was reopened. A special government group called the National Commission on Marijuana and Drug Abuse was appointed to study the problems of marijuana use and to make recommendations to the President. In 1972, they recommended that criminal penalties for the private possession and use of marijuana be abolished. They also recommended that sale of the drug remain illegal. In 1973, Oregon became the first state to decriminalize marijuana. This meant that users no longer faced a jail term but could be fined if convicted of possession. Sale of the drug remained illegal. Since that time, several other states have decriminalized private possession and use.

Medical researchers have found that marijuana may be useful in treating certain disorders such as glaucoma, high blood pressure, and chronic pain. (*See* EYE AND VISION; PAIN.) Some individuals have even been granted federal permission to use marijuana to treat some of these medical conditions.

Marijuana has many nicknames such as grass, pot, weed, or dope. Hashish, or hash, as it is commonly called, is also derived from the hemp plant. It is much stronger than marijuana, however, and is produced from the THC-rich resins of the plant. *See also* DRUG; HEMP.   A.J.C./F.W.S.

MARINE BIOLOGY (mə rēn′ bī äl′ ə jē) Marine biology is the study of living things in the oceans. The word "marine" refers to the ocean. Scientists who study marine biology are called marine biologists. They study microscopic organisms, seaweed, clams, lobsters, fish, birds, and mammals that live in or around the oceans. Today people are turning to the sea to obtain more energy, food, water, and minerals. Marine biologists are becoming more important as experts about the ocean and its resources. *See also* LIMNOLOGY; PLANKTON; OCEANOGRAPHY. S.R.G./R.J.B.

MARL (märl) Marl is loose soil that contains clay, sand, limestone, and large amounts of a chemical called calcium carbonate. Marl soils are formed in fresh or salt waters. The photosynthesis of plants in the water often speeds up the formation of marl. Shell marls contain the shells of dead sea animals like coral. (*See* CORAL.) Marl is a base—the opposite of an acid. Before artificial fertilizers were invented, marl was often spread on acidic soil to make it more fertile. *See also* CLAY; LIMESTONE; PH; PHOTOSYNTHESIS. S.R.G./R.J.B.

MARMOSET (mär′ mə set′) The marmoset is one of the smallest monkeys. It lives in the forests of Panama and South America. Marmosets vary in size. They are usually less than 30 cm [1 ft] in length, not including the tail. Most weigh less than 0.5 kg [1 lb]. The tails of most marmosets are longer than their bodies. Unlike many other monkeys of South America, the marmoset's tail is never prehensile (used for grasping).

Some marmosets have tufts of hair above their ears. Some have beards or mustaches. The golden or lion-headed marmoset (*Leontideus rosalia*) has soft, golden hair that resembles a lion's mane.

Marmosets live in groups, moving from tree to tree like squirrels. These monkeys move about only during the day. At night they sleep in trees. When startled, the marmoset quickly lets out a shrill cry. Marmosets feed mainly on fruits and insects.

Many marmosets have been captured to be sold as pets. Some species, such as the golden marmoset, have become endangered.

The golden marmoset is one of the smallest of the New World monkeys.

Many of the marmoset's forests have been and are being destroyed. J.J.A./J.J.M.

MARMOT (mär′ mət) The marmot, a rodent, is the largest member of the squirrel family. There are various kinds of marmots.

Marmots are mountain-dwelling rodents. They feed on grasses and other plants.

Most live in mountainous regions in North America and Europe, and in much of Asia.

Marmots living in North America range from about 30 to 61 cm [1 to 2 ft] in length, not including the tail. These animals have short legs, small ears, and furry tails. Most marmots have gray fur on the back, with reddish or yellowish orange fur covering their bellies. Marmots feed on grasses and other plants. These animals hibernate in burrows during the winter. The woodchuck is a kind of marmot that lives in fields and woods of the eastern United States. (*See* GROUNDHOG.)

J.J.A./J.J.M.

MARROW (mar′ ō) Marrow is the soft substance that fills the cavities of bones. It contains several different kinds of cell and may be red or yellow in color. It contains red and white blood cells of various types, fat cells, and connective tissue. It works like a factory to produce new blood cells for the body.

After birth, red blood cells, some white cells, and the fragments called platelets are formed entirely in the bone marrow. (Blood platelets are concerned with the clotting of blood.) In infants, all the bones are filled with red marrow making new blood cells. In adults, most of the bones contain yellow fatty marrow which does not make blood cells. Red marrow is left only in the sternum (breastbone), the ribs, bones of the spine, pelvis, and some skull bones. However, when the body needs extra blood cells, the yellow marrow in the other bones can become red marrow again. It starts to manufacture extra cells.

When a person has a blood disease, examining a sample of bone marrow under the microscope may show what is wrong. A small quantity is sucked from the center of a bone through a needle. Changes in the marrow occur in anemia, leukemia, and some kinds of cancer. *See also* BLOOD; BONE.

D.M.H.W./J.J.F.

MARS (märz) Mars is the fourth planet from the sun. Mars comes as close as 56 million km [35 million mi] to the earth. The only planet closer to the earth is Venus.

Mars has a diameter of 6,760 km [4,200 mi], which is about half the diameter of the earth. It takes Mars 687 days to make a complete rotation around the sun. A Martian day lasts 24 hours and 37 minutes, slightly longer than an earth day. The distance between the sun and Mars averages 227.7 million km [141.5 million mi].

Mars is much colder than the earth. The average temperature on Mars is about −62°C [−80°F]. At night, the temperature may drop to −101°C [−150°F]. The axis of Mars has a tilt of about 25°. This tilt is responsible for the Martian seasons. Scientists think that the summer daytime temperature at the Martian equator reaches 21°C [70°F].

The surface of Mars When viewed through a telescope, Mars seems to be made up of bright areas and dark areas. These areas constantly change shape. The bright areas, which cover about two-thirds of Mars, are reddish brown deserts. Scientists think that the deserts may contain limonite, a mineral which is also found in deserts on earth.

The dark areas are called maria, or seas, even though they contain no water. The maria appear bluish gray but seem to become greenish during the Martian spring and summer. During the Martian autumn and winter, some maria disappear completely. This variation may be caused by the blowing and settling of dust and sand.

The so-called Martian canals do not show up in the thousands of photographs of the Martian surface taken by American space probes. Instead, the photographs show irregular channels resembling dried-up riverbeds. In addition, the southern hemisphere appears to be heavily cratered, while the northern hemisphere is the site of some of the largest volcanoes in the solar system.

The north and south poles of Mars are

This picture of Mars was taken by the Viking 2 space probe, which landed on September 3, 1976, on Mars' Utopian Plain. The purpose of the probe was to analyze the soil and atmosphere and to send back photographs of this interesting planet. The information obtained indicates that there is no life on Mars: its atmosphere is thin, and its surface is exposed to lethal doses of ultraviolet radiation and to the chemical effects of highly oxidizing substances (such as hydrogen peroxide) produced by photochemistry. Another finding of the Viking probe is that what seem to be "canals" on Mars do not actually exist. In this picture one can see the high-gain antenna (the round object at the top of the picture), which is pointed towards the Earth. The field in front of Viking 2 is filled with red rocks and stretches to the horizon nearly 2 miles from the spacecraft. Scientists believe the colors of the Martian surface and sky in this picture represent their true colors. The picture shows the fine particles of red dust that have settled on the surface of the spacecraft. The salmon color of the sky is caused by dust particles suspended in the atmosphere. The three color-calibration charts mounted on Viking 2 are also visible. One is just to the right of the flag, the second is at the center bottom, and the third is to the right of the antenna's support arm. These charts help the scientists evaluate the colors in the photographs. Viking 2 was the second space probe to land on Mars. Viking 1, the first, touched down on July 20, 1976, at a dune field on Chryse Planita, 4600 miles away from Viking 2's landing place.

NASA

covered by white polar caps. These polar caps are composed of both solid carbon dioxide (dry ice) and water ice. The polar caps expand during the winter and contract during the summer.

The Martian atmosphere is much thinner than the earth's atmosphere. In 1976, Viking I analyzed the Martian atmosphere. It found it to contain 1 to 2 percent argon, 2 to 3 percent nitrogen, 95 percent carbon dioxide, and 0.3 percent oxygen. There is also a very small amount of water vapor. The Martian atmosphere has about 1 percent the density of the earth's atmosphere. This accounts for the vast temperature changes on Mars. Occasionally, thick clouds, possibly composed of water vapor, drift across the planet.

The moons of Mars Mars has two small moons, or satellites. Phobos, the larger moon, has a diameter of 23 km [14 mi]. It makes a complete orbit around Mars every 7½ hours. The smaller moon, Deimos, takes 30 hours to orbit Mars. The diameter of Deimos is 10 km [6 mi]. Both moons were discovered by the American astronomer Asaph Hall in 1877.

Space probes to Mars Several unmanned space probes have studied Mars since 1965. Four American space probes—Mariner IV, Mariner VI, Mariner VII, and Mariner IX—all orbited but did not land on Mars. These probes sent photographs of the Martian moons, dust storms, and of the previously unknown Martian craters.

In 1976, the American Viking I and Viking II space probes landed on the Martian surface. They transmitted superb photographs of the Martian landscape. Viking I and Viking II also analyzed the soil and atmosphere of Mars. None of the space probes have detected any evidence of life on Mars. *See also* EXOBIOLOGY; PLANET.   J.M.C./C.R.

MARSH GAS (märsh gas) Marsh gas is an inflammable gas that forms when plants decay in places where there is very little air. The gas consists of methane, usually with small amounts of nitrogen and carbon dioxide. Marsh gas is so called because it is found around stagnant water and swamps. Pockets of the gas form at the bottom of marshes, lakes, and ponds. The bubbles that rise to the surface when the bottom is disturbed are bubbles of marsh gas. *See also* METHANE.

J.J.A./J.M.

MARSUPIAL (mär sü′ pē əl) A marsupial is any of 250 species of pouch-bearing mammals belonging to the order Marsupialia. They are relatively primitive mammals because the unborn young are not nourished by a placenta as are most other mammals. (*See* PLACENTA.) Newborn marsupials are very tiny and are not developed enough to survive outside the pouch, or marsupium. After birth, the young marsupial crawls through the mother's fur from the birth canal to the pouch. Once inside the pouch, it attaches to a teat, or nipple, from the mammary (milk-producing) glands. The baby stays attached to the teat until it is developed enough to leave the pouch. If there are more offspring than there are teats, the extra offspring will die. They do not share the teats as do many other mammals. The young marsupial is not able to suck milk from the teat. Instead, milk is squirted into its mouth at regular intervals. After leaving the pouch, the young marsupial stays near its mother and may, if frightened, hide in the pouch.

Most marsupials live in Australasia, an area which includes Australia, New Zealand, New Guinea, and neighboring islands. Some other marsupials live in South America. The only marsupial native to the United States is the Virginia opossum. (*See* OPOSSUM.)

Marsupials were most numerous and probably lived on all the continents during the Mesozoic era, 225 to 265 million years ago. During the course of evolution, they were replaced by placentals, mammals with

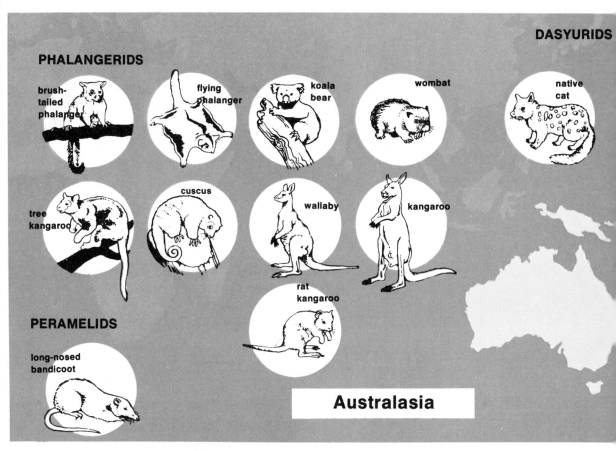

The cuscus, often called an Australian opossum, is a phalangerid marsupial. It lives in trees and has a long prehensile tail which is capable of grasping objects such as this tree branch.

placentas. It is only because of the isolation of Australasia and South America that marsupials were not forced into extinction by the more advanced mammals. Some of the common marsupials are the bandicoot, kangaroo, wombat, koala, opossum, Tasmanian devil, and wallaby.

Since 1900, the number of marsupials has decreased greatly. Some species that were once numerous are now extinct. This has been mostly due to human beings who introduced new carnivorous mammals (predators such as dogs, cats, and foxes) into previously safe areas. In addition, many farmers hunt or trap marsupials (especially kangaroos) because they consider these animals to be pests. *See also* EVOLUTION; MAMMAL; MONOTREME.

A.J.C./J.J.M.

MARTEN (märt' ən) The marten is a slender, fur-covered mammal belonging to the weasel family, Mustelidae. Martens live in the forest regions of North America, Europe,

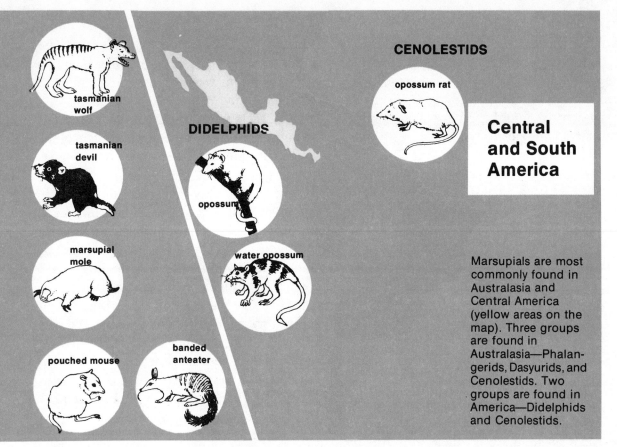

CENOLESTIDS

opossum rat

Central and South America

DIDELPHIDS

tasmanian wolf

tasmanian devil

marsupial mole

opossum

water opossum

pouched mouse

banded anteater

Marsupials are most commonly found in Australasia and Central America (yellow areas on the map). Three groups are found in Australasia—Phalangerids, Dasyurids, and Cenolestids. Two groups are found in America—Didelphids and Cenolestids.

and Asia. Martens are most often solitary.

The pine marten (*Martes americana*), sometimes called the American sable, is probably the best known of the American martens. It is about 61 cm [2 ft] in length, including the tail. The pine marten feeds on mice, squirrel, and birds. This species has soft, grayish brown fur. From November to March, the pine marten's coat is very thick. During this season, marten trappers in Canada and the United States kill about 30,000 of these animals. The fur is sold for use in coats, muffs, and hats.

Breeding usually takes place in the summer and one to five young are born the following March or April. Females probably breed in the summer of the year following their birth. *See also* SABLE; WEASEL. J.J.A./J.J.M.

MARTIN (märt′ ən) Martin is the name for several types of small birds belonging to the swallow family. The purple martin (*Progne subis*) is widely known in North America. In winter, the purple martin migrates to Central and South America.

Purple martins often live in birdhouses which people have made for them. Martins often return to the same birdhouse year after year. Some martins, however, build their nests in trees far away from people.

The female martin lays from three to eight white eggs. Martins help people by eating ants, flies, and other winged insect pests. In New England, sparrows and starlings have driven most of the martins from their homes.

J.J.A./L.L.S.

MASER (mā′zər) The word maser is short for microwave amplification by stimulated emission of radiation. Microwaves are a form of electromagnetic radiation. A maser is an instrument that produces microwaves.

Microwaves are similar to radio waves. (*See* MICROWAVE.) The frequency of a wave is the number of times that it vibrates in a second. A maser produces microwaves with just one frequency and not a range of frequencies. For this reason, the maser is used as a very accurate timing device. It can be accurate to one second in 100,000 years. Masers are also used in astronomy. They are used to strengthen, or amplify, radio waves coming from stars and planets.

The maser was invented in 1953 by the American scientist Charles H. Townes. Seven years later, a similar instrument called a laser was invented. The laser produces light instead of microwaves. *See also* LASER.

M.E./L.L.R.

MASS (mas) Mass is the amount of matter in a body. Mass is very similar to weight. (*See* WEIGHT.) There is, however, an important difference between weight and mass. Weight is caused by the force of gravity acting on a body. If the gravity changes, the weight changes. Mass, on the other hand, does not depend on gravity. It remains constant. For example, on the moon the mass of a body is the same as its mass on the earth. But its weight is not the same. Gravity on the moon is six times weaker than it is on the earth. Therefore, the weight of the body is six times less.

Physicists once thought that the mass of a body could never change. We know now that this is not quite true. The theory of relativity states that the mass of a body increases with its velocity. (*See* RELATIVITY.) For low speeds, the increase is very small.

The theory of relativity shows that mass is a form of energy. In special cases, mass can be turned into energy. A small mass produces a huge amount of energy. This happens in nuclear weapons, in the sun, and in other stars. This energy is called thermonuclear energy. (*See* THERMONUCLEAR ENERGY.)

M.E./J.D.

MASS ACTION, LAW OF The law of mass action (mas′ ak′ shən) is concerned with the speed at which chemical reactions occur. It states that the rate at which a substance reacts is proportional to its concentra-

tion. The law is only true if the temperature is kept constant. The concentration is measured as the number of moles of the substance in a liter of solution. A mole is a certain number of molecules. (*See* MOLE.) As an example, hydrogen reacts with oxygen to form water. If the concentration of either the hydrogen or the oxygen is doubled, then the reaction goes twice as fast.

The law of mass action was discovered in connection with chemical equilibrium. As an example of chemical equilibrium, nitrogen and hydrogen can combine to form the gas ammonia. At the same time, ammonia breaks down into nitrogen and hydrogen. These two reactions take place at the same time. Nitrogen and hydrogen combine together at a certain rate, and ammonia breaks down at a certain rate. These rates depend on the temperature and the pressure. At a certain temperature and pressure, the two rates are equal. This is called chemical equilibrium. The law of mass action allows chemists to calculate the concentrations of the gases at equilibrium.

M.E./J.D.

MASS PRODUCTION (mas′ prə dək′ shən) Mass production is the manufacturing of the same or similar articles quickly and continuously. Mass production makes it possible to manufacture more things faster. This lowers the selling price and creates an even larger demand by buyers. Mass production also means that whenever a part on a mass-produced article breaks down, a replacement part that fits perfectly can be obtained.

Mass-produced articles are made in factories that use assembly line methods. Workers are stationed at many points along a moving conveyor system. (*See* CONVEYOR.) As the product to be put together moves along the line, each worker or group of workers performs a single operation or installs a part. By the time the product reaches the end of the assembly line, it may have been worked on by 100 workers. Some assembly lines are com-

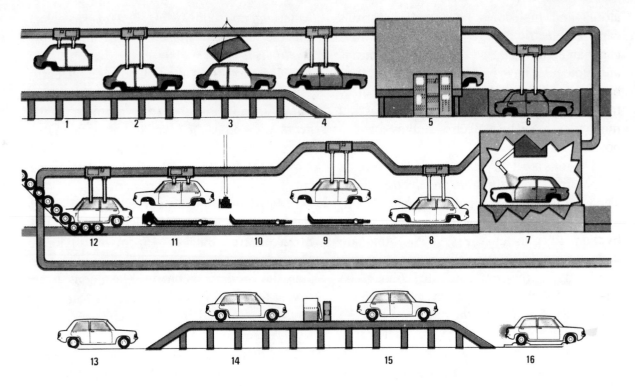

Mass production of cars is carried out on a production line like the one shown here. First, the body is assembled (1, 2, 3, 4) starting with the frame and finishing with the doors. The metal is treated to prevent rust (5) and then dipped in a vat of primer paint (6). The final color is sprayed on (7). Next, the internal parts, such as the steering gear and lights, are put in (8) and then the transmission and engine are put in (9,10,11). Once the wheels have been attached (12) the car is driven (13) onto a stand where final connections to the steering and electrical parts can be made. Finally, the tank is filled with gasoline (15) and the car is given a complete test drive (16).

pletely automated. Machines automatically perform all the tasks.

A wide range of experts participates in mass production, including design engineers, planners, time study engineers, statisticians, inventory controllers, expeditors, machinists, and skilled craftsmen of all types.

The United States leads the world in mass production. Nearly every article made in the U.S.—from freezers to automobiles—is manufactured by mass production methods.

Although Henry Ford, founder of the Ford Motor Co., is generally credited with using the first large-scale assembly line in the early

1900s, mass production assembly lines actually began much earlier. Eli Whitney, the inventor of the cotton gin, built special machine tools to mass produce muskets for the Continental Army in 1800. Until then, muskets had been built by hand, one at a time. Once Whitney had his machines set up, he could produce 10,000 muskets during the time it took a regular gunsmith to produce one. *See also* AUTOMATION; AUTOMOBILE.

W.R.P./R.W.L.

MASS SPECTROGRAPH (mas spek′ trə graf′) A mass spectrograph is an instrument that is used to analyze substances. It finds out what different kinds of atoms and molecules are in a substance. It also finds out how much of each kind the substance contains.

The first step in the analysis is to change the substance into a gas. Then the atoms and molecules in the substance are ionized. (*See* IONS AND IONIZATION.) This means that electrons are added or removed from the atoms and molecules. This is done by bombarding the gas with a beam of electrons, changing the atoms and molecules into ions. Electrons carry an electric charge. Therefore, the ions carry an electric charge as well. If the atoms and molecules have had electrons added, they have a negative charge. This is because electrons have a negative charge. If the atoms and molecules have lost electrons, they have a positive charge.

The ions are then accelerated. This is done by passing them through an electric field. Then the ions pass through a magnetic field. Since the ions are charged, they are deflected by the field. If the charge is positive, they are deflected one way. If it is negative, they are deflected in the opposite direction. The amount of deflection depends on the masses of the ions. The heavier the mass, the less the deflection. This spreads the ions out. Only those ions with the same mass and charge stay together. The ions then hit a photographic plate. Different ions hit the plate in different places. The identity of each ion is discovered by seeing where it hits the plate. Electronics has made mass spectrometry possible using many new and different techniques.   M.E./J.T.

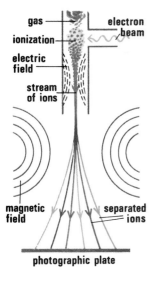

How a mass spectrograph works. A substance is changed into gas and passes into a vacuum chamber. A beam of electrons changes the gas atoms and molecules into ions. An electric field then accelerates the ions. A magnetic field attracts the ions according to their mass, separating ions of different masses. Separated ions hit different areas of a photographic plate, which records the amounts of various atoms and molecules in the substance.

MASTODON (mäs′ tə dän′) The mastodon is an extinct, elephantlike animal belonging to the family Mammutidae. There were over 1,000 species of mastodons, including the American mastodon (*Mastodon americanum*) and the European mastodon (*Mastodon angustidens*).

Mastodons first appeared during the early Miocene epoch, about 25,000,000 years ago. They ranged throughout the northern continents. Scientists believe that American Indians lived with the mastodons in North America until the end of the Pleistocene epoch, about 15,000 years ago.

Mastodons had curved tusks and elephantlike trunks. Their teeth were about 8 cm [3 in] wide and 15 cm [6 in] long. Mastodons were shorter and had smaller ears than the modern elephant. Mastodons were covered with long, reddish brown hair.

Mastodons fed on plants and leaves. They were related to the larger mammoth. The reason for their extinction a few thousand years ago is still unknown. *See also* MIOCENE EPOCH.   J.M.C./J.J.M.

MATCH (mach) A match is a narrow piece of wood or cardboard with a tip made of a chemical mixture that burns easily. Matches are used to produce fire. When the tip is rubbed against a rough or specially prepared surface the chemicals burst into flame and ignite the match. There are two main types of matches: strike-anywhere matches and safety matches.

Strike-anywhere matches light when rubbed against any rough surface. The match is basically a wood splint, or shaft, about 8 cm [3 in] long, and about 0.3 cm [0.12 in] in diameter. It may have a tip of two colors, red and white or blue and white. The small white tip, called the eye, contains a firing substance made chiefly of sesquisulfide of phosphorus. The remainder of the tip, the red or blue part, does not ignite by being rubbed against a rough surface. It only burns when the flaming eye sets it afire. It carries the flame to the rest of the matchstick, which is coated with paraffin to make it burn faster. Wooden strike-anywhere matches are made by automatic machines that manufacture and package more than a million matches an hour.

Safety matches can only be lighted by striking them against a special surface. The surface is usually located on the box or folder in which the matches come. The tip of the safety match is made of a substance containing chlorate of potash. Chlorate of potash has a low kindling point of 182°C [360°F]. When it rubs against the striking surface, which is a compound of red phosphorus and sand, it quickly ignites. The most common type of safety matches are book matches. They are made of paper and bound into a folding paper cover. The striking surface is on the outside. The user is supposed to close the cover before striking. This prevents the other matches in the pack from lighting.

The first match was made in 1827 by John Walker, an English pharmacist. It was a splint of wood about 8 cm [3 in] long and tipped with antimony sulfide, chlorate of potash, gum arabic, and starch. The match burst into flames with a series of small explosions that showered its user with sparks. The first safety matches were invented in 1844 by Gustave E. Pasch, a Swedish chemist. Book matches were introduced in 1892 by Joshua Pusey, a Philadelphia lawyer.

The United States ranks as the world's leading producer of matches. France, Russia, and Sweden also have large match industries.

W.R.P./A.D.

MATHEMATICS

Mathematics (math′ ə mat′ iks) is divided into two major branches: pure mathematics and applied mathematics. Pure mathematics is the study of quantity. It also studies the different ways in which quantities can be combined. There are many different kinds of quantities studied by pure mathematicians. An example is numbers. Numbers can be combined by addition, subtraction, multiplication, and division. The study of numbers and how they combine is called arithmetic. Sometimes symbols are used to represent numbers. The study of how these symbols behave is called algebra. The study of shapes, such as triangles and circles, is called geometry. (See ALGEBRA; ARITHMETIC; GEOMETRY.)

Since the end of the 1800s, many new branches of mathematics have been developed. These branches are based on quantities called sets. (See SET THEORY.) These new branches of mathematics are called modern mathematics. By using sets, modern mathematics can solve many more problems than the old mathematics.

Pure mathematics is not a branch of science. Science studies the real world. Pure mathematics is concerned only with quantities. Whether these quantities occur in the real world does not concern a pure mathematician. Many quantities in pure mathematics have no real existence. They exist only in pure mathematics and not in the real world. Nevertheless, many ideas in pure mathematics are used in science, especially in physics.

The other main branch of mathematics is applied mathematics. Applied mathematics uses ideas from pure mathematics to solve practical problems. Most of applied mathematics is concerned with problems in physics. This is because physics is the most mathematical of all sciences. Applied mathematics also studies biology, economics, and social problems.

History of mathematics Numbers have been used for thousands of years. By 3000 B.C. the Egyptians and Babylonians were measuring lengths and using numbers for calculating. The Babylonians were the first to divide the day into hours, minutes, and seconds. We still use their system. They also divided the circle into 360 degrees.

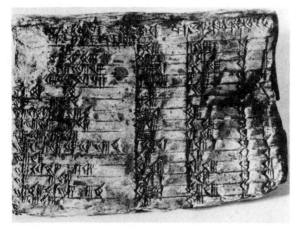

This Babylonian mathematics tablet, inscribed in about 1600 B.C., demonstrates the calculation of the diagonal of a square from its sides.

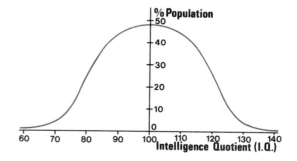

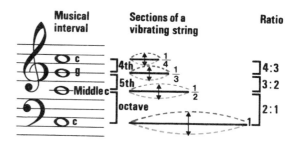

Pythagoras showed that musical intervals are made by sections of a vibrating string whose lengths are related in simple ratios.

The ancient Greeks were very advanced in mathematics. The first great Greek mathematician was Thales of Miletus who lived from about 640 to 546 B.C. He studied geometry. One of the greatest of the Greek mathematicians was Pythagoras. Pythagoras and his order made many important discoveries in geometry. (*See* PYTHAGORAS' THEOREM.) They also discovered a relation between the notes of a musical scale. This is illustrated above right.

In 300 B.C. a mathematician named Euclid wrote a famous book called *The Elements*. This book contained everything that was known about geometry at that time. His book was still being used in schools in the 1800s.

The greatest Greek mathematician was Archimedes. (See ARCHIMEDES.) He died in 212 B.C. He made many discoveries in both mathematics and physics. He discovered the laws of levers and hydrostatics. (*See* HYDROSTATICS; MACHINE, SIMPLE.)

During the last few centuries B.C. the civilization of Greeks declined. Their knowledge was preserved by the Arabs. This knowledge passed on to Europe in about 1000 A.D. Until the 1600s mathematicians in Europe made very few discoveries of their own.

Then, in the 1600s, Galileo made discoveries in dynamics and John Napier invented logarithms. (*See* GALILEO; NAPIER, JOHN.) In the same century, calculus was invented by two people at the same time. They were the English scientist, Sir Isaac Newton, and Gottfried Leibnitz, a German philosopher. Calculus is a very powerful method of solving problems. With calculus, mathematics developed very fast in the next few hundred years. Another important invention during the 1600s was coordinate geometry. It was invented by a Frenchman, René Descartes. (*See* DESCARTES, RENÉ.)

The most important mathematician during the 1700s and 1800s was a German, Carl Friedrich Gauss. He lived from 1777 to 1855. He made important discoveries in all branches of mathematics, particularly in algebra, probability, and statistics. (*See* PROBABILITY; STATISTICS.) He also made discoveries in physics and surveying.

During the 1800s, mathematicians started to apply logic to mathematics. This made mathematics much more powerful. It also led to the use of sets in mathematics. Originally, sets were used only in logic. Whole new areas of mathematics were developed using sets, such as topology and game theory. (*See* TOPOLOGY.) Game theory was invented by an American, John von Neumann. Game theory played an important part in the development of computers. It is also used in economics and in working out military strategies.

M.E./S.P.A.

MATRIX (mā′ triks) In mathematics, a matrix is a "box" of numbers. For example:

$$\begin{pmatrix} 1 & 3 & 0 \\ 2 & 1 & 5 \end{pmatrix}$$

is a matrix. It is called a 2×3 matrix because it has two rows and three columns.

$$\begin{pmatrix} 2 & 1 \\ 3 & 4 \end{pmatrix}$$

is another matrix. It has two rows and two columns and is a 2×2 matrix. It is called a square matrix because it has the same number of rows and columns. A matrix can have any number of rows and columns.

Matrices are widely used in mathematics and science. They are frequently used to show the connection between two objects or situations. For example, the diagram below has two islands, A and B. Island A has two air-

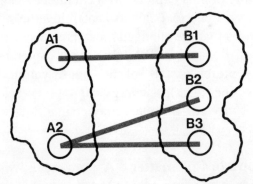

ports, A1 and A2. Island B has three airports, B1, B2, and B3. The red lines show the air

routes that connect the airports. These routes can be represented by a matrix. 0 means that there is no route between two airports. 1 means that there is one air route between two airports. 2 means that there are two routes, and so on.

$$\begin{array}{c} \\ A1 \\ A2 \end{array} \begin{array}{ccc} B1 & B2 & B3 \\ \begin{pmatrix} 1 & 0 & 0 \\ 0 & 1 & 1 \end{pmatrix} \end{array}$$

The top left entry means that there is one route from A1 to B1. The top right entry means that there is no route from A1 to B3, and so on.

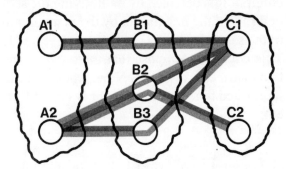

Now another island, C, is added. It has two airports, C1 and C2. The air routes between B and C are shown in red lines. The air routes can be shown by another matrix:

$$\begin{array}{c} \\ B1 \\ B2 \\ B3 \end{array} \begin{array}{cc} C1 & C2 \\ \begin{pmatrix} 1 & 0 \\ 1 & 1 \\ 1 & 0 \end{pmatrix} \end{array}$$

An aircraft can fly from airport A1 to B1 and then to C1. Therefore, there is a route from A1 to C1. Similarly, there are two routes from A2 to C1. The aircraft can fly from A2 to B2 or B3 and then to C1. The air routes between A and C are represented by the matrix:

$$\begin{array}{c} \\ A1 \\ A2 \end{array} \begin{array}{cc} C1 & C2 \\ \begin{pmatrix} 1 & 0 \\ 2 & 1 \end{pmatrix} \end{array}$$

This matrix can also be formed by combining the other two matrices:

$$\begin{pmatrix} 1 & 0 & 0 \\ 0 & 1 & 1 \end{pmatrix} \begin{pmatrix} 1 & 0 \\ 1 & 1 \\ 1 & 0 \end{pmatrix} = \begin{pmatrix} 1 & 0 \\ 2 & 1 \end{pmatrix}$$

This is called multiplication of matrices. The AC matrix equals the AB matrix multiplied by the BC matrix. In multiplication, a row in the first matrix is multiplied by a column in the second matrix. The first row times the first column is $1 \times 1 + 0 \times 1 + 0 \times 1$. This equals 1. This number goes into the first row and the first column of the answer. This is the top left-hand position of the matrix. The bottom left number is in the second row and the first column. It is obtained by multiplying the second row of the first matrix by the first column of the second. This is $0 \times 1 + 1 \times 1 + 1 \times 1$. This equals 2. Suppose that the order of the two matrices is reversed. Now, when they are multiplied together, the answer is very different:

$$\begin{pmatrix} 1 & 0 \\ 1 & 1 \\ 1 & 0 \end{pmatrix} \begin{pmatrix} 1 & 0 & 0 \\ 0 & 1 & 1 \end{pmatrix} = \begin{pmatrix} 1 & 0 & 0 \\ 1 & 1 & 1 \\ 1 & 0 & 0 \end{pmatrix}$$

The matrix is a different size from the one before. In the first case, the first matrix had two rows and the second had two columns. Therefore the final matrix had two rows and two columns. Now the first matrix has three rows and the second has three columns. The final matrix has three rows and three columns. The order in which matrices are multiplied is very important.

Two matrices can also be added. This can only be done if they have the same number of rows and columns. They are then added by adding the number in the same places in each matrix. For example:

$$\begin{pmatrix} 1 & 2 \\ 1 & 0 \end{pmatrix} + \begin{pmatrix} 2 & 0 \\ 3 & 4 \end{pmatrix} = \begin{pmatrix} 3 & 2 \\ 4 & 4 \end{pmatrix}$$

The top left number in each matrix is 1 and 2. They are added to give 3. This becomes the top left number in the answer. Matrices can also be subtracted from each other. But they cannot be divided into each other.

M.E./S.P.A.

MATTER (mat' ər) Everything that can be seen or touched is made of matter. The air we breathe is matter. Most scientists define matter as anything that occupies space. Scientists also say that matter has inertia. Inertia is a resistance to change of position or motion. All objects are made up of matter. The measure of the matter in an object is called its mass. But scientists usually define mass as a measure of inertia. The pull of the earth on an object gives that object weight. But weight can change. An object on the moon weighs only one-sixth as much as it does on earth. Its mass, however, would be the same. (*See* GRAVITY.)

People may become aware of energy when they feel heat from a fire or see light from an electric bulb. Such processes involve energy. Scientists usually define energy as the ability to do work, or to move matter. (*See* ENERGY.) Until the time of Albert Einstein, scientists believed that matter could not be destroyed or created. This idea was called the conservation of matter. But Einstein proved that mass and energy are interconvertible. Matter can be changed into energy. Energy can be changed into matter. For example, matter changes into energy when radioactive elements disintegrate (break down) or when atomic bombs explode. If a chemical change gives off energy (such as heat), then the substances that are changed must have lost some mass. Because of Einstein's work, scientists now prefer to talk of the conservation of mass energy. Mass energy cannot be created or destroyed. But each may change into the other.

Properties of matter A property is what can be said about a thing to tell how it looks, feels, smells, tastes, or acts under certain conditions. For example, hardness is a property of stone, and wetness is a property of water. All matter has properties. The properties are divided into two kinds—physical and chemical.

Physical properties are those that can be found by direct use of the senses and by weighing and measuring. Color, smell, shape, roughness, smoothness, sweetness, and saltiness are examples of physical properties. Elasticity (stretchiness or springiness) and tension (how much force is needed to make a thing break) are physical properties that can be measured. Another physical property of matter is density, which is the amount of matter in a unit of volume (amount of space). Because of the difference in density, a tennis ball weighs less than a rock of the same size. Solubility and conductivity are also physical properties. Solubility is the ability of one kind of matter to dissolve in another. Conductivity is the ability of matter to conduct heat or electricity. (*See* CONDUCTION, HEAT; CONDUCTION OF ELECTRICITY.)

Chemical properties of matter describe how a substance acts when it undergoes a chemical change. For example, one chemical property of oxygen is its ability to combine with many metals to form compounds called oxides. Oxygen combines with iron. When this happens, a new substance, called iron oxide (rust) appears.

Certain properties make us call certain types of matter by a special name, such as gold, chlorine, or carbon. They are determined by the number of protons (positive particles) in each nucleus and by the number of electrons (negative particles) surrounding each nucleus of the atoms of this matter. Oxygen, for example, has eight protons in the nuclei of its atoms. (See ATOM; ELEMENT.)

States of matter   In its familiar form, matter can exist in three physical states—a solid, a liquid, or a gas. A substance can take on these various states depending on its temperature. For instance, water (a liquid at room tempera-ture) can be frozen solid to ice at 0°C [32°F] or turned to a gaseous steam at 100°C [212°F]. Scientists also define a fourth state of matter, called plasma. Plasma exists under special conditions. (*See* STATES OF MATTER.)

J.J.A./J.T.

MAXWELL, JAMES CLERK (1831–1879) James Maxwell (mak′ swel′) was a Scottish physicist. He was born and educated at Edinburgh. He was a brilliant mathematician. When he was only 15 he had a paper published by the Royal Society of Edinburgh.

Maxwell was interested in energy. First he worked on heat, then on electricity and magnetism. He came up with the idea of electromagnetic waves. Using his mathematical skill, he predicted forms of electromagnetic radiation that had not been discovered. He said there would be a whole range of waves, all with different wavelengths. Radio waves were discovered later. They fitted in with his theory perfectly.

Maxwell also worked on light. He studied color vision and developed the electromagnetic theory of light. He became the first Cavendish Professor of Physics at Cambridge in 1871. *See also* ELECTROMAGNETIC RADIATION; LIGHT; SPECTRUM.   C.M./D.G.F.

James Clerk Maxwell

MAYAN CIVILIZATION (mī′ ən siv′ ə lə zā′ shən) The Mayan civilization was an advanced society of Central American Indians. It flourished from about A.D. 200 to 800. The Mayans lived in parts of the dense jungles that are Belize, El Salvador, Guatemala, Honduras, and Mexico.

The Mayans built huge stone pyramids with small temples at the top. Leading up to the temple was a large staircase. These pyramids were used only for religious functions.

The Mayans were very interested in astronomy. They worked out tables to predict eclipses of the sun. They also studied the orbit of the planet Venus.

The Mayans developed a calender. They had three types of years: a 360-day year, a 365-day year, and a 260-day year. The 260-day year had special religious meaning.

The Mayans devised a system of numbers based on the number 20. They had a symbol equivalent to the modern zero.

The Mayans were the only American Indians to devise an advanced system of writing. Their writing consisted of symbols representing sounds and ideas. This system of writing is a form of hieroglyphics. The Mayans put their writings into bark-cloth books.

The Mayans lived by farming. They grew corn, squash, sweet potatoes, tobacco, cotton, and cacao. Some Mayans raised bees for honey.

The Mayan civilization had passed its peak when the first Europeans arrived in the New World. In the 1500s, Spanish troops conquered the remaining Mayans and burned all but three of their bark-cloth books. This event marked the end of the Mayan civilization. *See also* INDIAN CIVILIZATION.

J.M.C./S.O.

MAYFLY (mā′ flī) The mayfly is any of about 1,500 species of insects belonging to the order Ephemeroptera. The adult is usually less than 4 cm [1.5 in] long, including tails. It has four wings: two large, triangular forewings and two, smaller, oval hindwings. The adult lives for only a few hours or days—just long enough to mate and (for the female) to lay eggs. The adult has two or three threadlike tails. It has no mouth, and is unable to eat during its short life. Because of its short life, the mayfly is sometimes called the dayfly.

The eggs are usually laid in streams or ponds. They hatch into two or three-tailed nymphs which live underwater and breathe through gills. (*See* NYMPH.) The nymphs feed on algae and other underwater plants and may live for as long as two or three years in this form. After molting many times, the nymph comes to the surface, sheds its skin, and becomes a subimago, or dun. The subimago is a winged creature that is a stage between the nymph and the adult. The mayfly is the only insect to undergo this stage as part of incomplete metamorphosis. (*See* METAMORPHOSIS.) Within a few hours, the subimago molts again and becomes an adult.

Although mayflies are most common in May and June, they may be seen as late as in September or October. The nymphs are a source of food for fish and are sometimes used as bait by fishermen. Fishermen often make artificial lures which look like mayflies. *See also* INSECT; MOLTING.   A.J.C./J.E.R.

Mayflies belong to the order Ephemeroptera. Mayfly eggs hatch into naiads (above, lower left) which live in water one to three years, molting several times before becoming adults.

MEADOWLARK (med′ ō lärk′) The meadowlark, which is not a true lark, is a common North American bird belonging to the family

Icteridae. The family also includes blackbirds and orioles. The meadowlark is usually found in meadows, grassy fields, and marshes and is about the size of a robin. The meadowlark, however, has a thicker body, longer bill, and shorter tail. The back and wings are brown marked with black. White outer tail feathers are seen when the bird is in flight. The throat and underparts are bright yellow. A large black crescent marks the breast.

The meadowlark builds its nest on the ground. A roof of grass often covers the nest to hide the eggs. The female lays three to seven white eggs with rust colored spots. Meadowlarks feed on waste grain. They also feed on many insects that are harmful to people.

The western meadowlark (*Sturnella neglecta*) and the eastern meadowlark (*Sturnella magna*) are the two types of meadowlarks. The meadowlark has a clear, tuneful whistle. The song of the western meadowlark is considered especially pleasant.   J.J.A./L.L.S.

MEASLES (mē′ zəlz) Measles is a disease caused by a virus. It is very infectious and occurs throughout the world. Most children in the United States and Europe catch the disease before they reach the age of ten. Fortunately, it is usually a very mild disease. The first symptoms are the same as those of the common cold. The patient is feverish and has a cough. The eyes and nose are inflamed, and the throat may be sore. Four days later, measles spots appear. They are small pink spots that spread in a rash from the neck and forehead to the rest of the body. The spots grow in size and join to form blotches. Then the rash disappears. At the end of nine or ten days, it has completely gone.

Epidemics of measles occur every two years or so. Once a person has had the disease, he or she cannot catch it again. The person becomes immune. Another way of producing immunity is by means of a vaccine. A single injection can be given when a person is two years old. Since vaccine was introduced in the United States in 1963, the number of children who catch the disease has been reduced by nine-tenths. It may be possible one day to get rid of the disease completely. *See also* EPIDEMIC; IMMUNITY; VACCINE.   D.M.H.W./J.J.F.

MEASUREMENT (mezh′ ər mənt) Measurement is the process of finding out how many units there are in something. These units include meters, inches, grams, pounds, and hours. Measurement is one of humanity's oldest skills.

Almost everyone uses measurement daily. The food we eat, the clothes we wear, the work we do, and the games we play involve measurement. For example, shoppers buy cloth by the meter or yard and meat by the kilogram or pound. Many workers are paid by the hour. A football team must gain 10 yards for a first down. An athlete who runs 100 meters in the shortest time wins the race.

People also use measurement to help them understand one another and to work together easily. A man could describe himself as being tall and heavy. But he would do better by describing himself as 6 ft 6 in tall and weighing 250 pounds. In the same way, contractors building a house can order a door that measures 30 inches wide, and they know it will fit the doorway built for it.

Many measurements are made by comparing the object to be measured with a scale of units on a measuring tool. A ruler, for example, is one of the most common measuring tools. Clocks, scales, tape measures, speedometers, and thermometers are other commonly used measuring devices.

Sometimes it is not practical to use a measuring tool to measure an object. Then the measurement must be made indirectly. For example, the amount of water in a swimming pool can be determined mathematically by finding the volume of the pool in cubic units. This indirect method is quicker and easier than dipping all the water out of the pool with a measured container.

Surveyors indirectly measure long distances on land by measuring angles and by applying mathematical principles such as trigonometry. Astronomers also measure indirectly the distances to the stars and planets. *See also* INSTRUMENT, SCIENTIFIC; NAVIGATION; TIME. W.R.P./R.W.L.

MECHANICAL DRAWING (mi kan′ i kəl drȯ′ ing) Whenever a product is made, an accurate detailed drawing of it is needed. These drawings are called mechanical drawings. They are widely used in industry and engineering. Mechanical drawings show the product from several different angles so that its shape may be seen. Sometimes they have sections through the product to show the inside. For a large or complicated structure, such as a ship, hundreds of drawings may be needed. Some of these drawings show the design of individual parts. Others show how these parts fit together.

Mechanical drawings are made by people called draftsmen. Draftsmen work with many different instruments, such as set squares, dividers, protractors, and compasses. These instruments enable them to draw a

design very accurately and to scale. The scale of a drawing may be, for example, 1 to 10 cm [.4 to 4 in]. This means that 1 cm on the drawing represents 10 cm on the structure itself. Usually a draftsman draws an object from the front, the side, and the top. A view from the top is called the plan. The views from the side and the front are called the elevation. Another kind of mechanical drawing is the isometric drawing. This shows the whole object, with all its parts drawn to the same scale. M.E./S.P.A.

MECHANICS (mi kan′ iks) Mechanics is the study of forces and how they affect bodies. It is concerned with such things as the flight of airplanes, stresses on bridges, and the motion of engines.

Classical mechanics is divided into a number of branches. The action of forces on solid bodies is studied in dynamics and statics. Dynamics is concerned with forces that cause bodies to move. Statics is the study of forces acting on bodies that are at rest or moving with constant velocity. Another branch of mechanics is called fluid dynamics. Fluid mechanics is divided into several branches, including hydrodynamics,

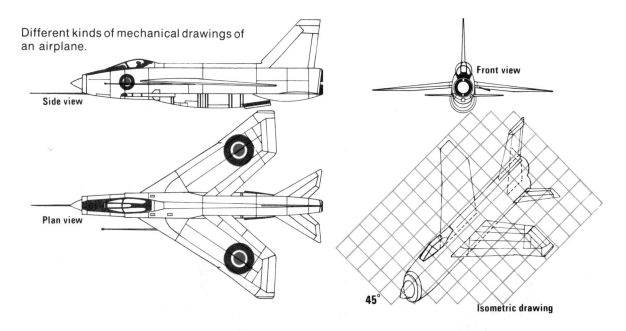

Different kinds of mechanical drawings of an airplane.

Side view

Plan view

Front view

45°

Isometric drawing

hydrostatics, and aerodynamics. Hydrodynamics is the study of the motion of a fluid under a force. Hydrostatics is the study of fluids at rest. Aerodynamics is the study of the effects of air on aircraft and missiles.

The basic laws of classical mechanics were studied about 300 years ago by Galileo and Sir Isaac Newton. (See GALILEO; NEWTON, SIR ISAAC.) These ideas remained unchanged until this century. Then Albert Einstein produced his theory of relativity. (See EINSTEIN, ALBERT.) His theory changed the study of mechanics. However, the older mechanics of Newton and Galileo is still used today. In normal situations it is still very accurate. *See also* DYNAMICS; FLUID MECHANICS.

M.E./J.T.

MEDICAL ENGINEERING (med′ i kəl en′ jə nir′ ing) Medical engineering is the construction and use of machines and equipment to help identify and treat diseases. It is sometimes called bio-medical engineering, or bioengineering. When an artificial part is used to replace one of the body's own parts, this is also known as prosthetics or spare-part surgery.

Machines for diagnosis Diagnosis is the identification of diseases. To aid doctors in this task, there are many different machines and devices. Some of them are designed to "see" inside the body. They produce pictures of internal organs and other parts that cannot be examined easily.

One of the most familiar aids is the X-ray machine. (*See* X RAY.) X rays travel right through the body. Dense parts of the body

The incubator is an example of medical engineering.

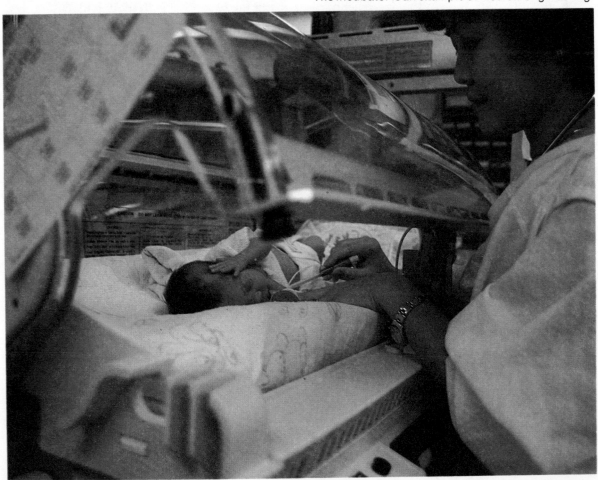

tend to stop X rays from passing through. These show up as light areas on an X-ray film or screen. This makes broken bones easy to see. By using substances that prevent X rays from passing through, it is possible to show the outlines of other internal structures like the intestines and kidneys.

Sound waves may also be used to make pictures of the inside of the body. They are useful when the use of X rays could be harmful. The sound waves that are used are of very short wavelength. (*See* ULTRASONIC.) They may be sent right through the body, like X rays, or reflected back as echoes.

Infrared rays (heat) from different parts of the body can be used to make photographs. They show up areas that are unusually warm or cold. They help to diagnose tumors, inflamed joints, and blocked blood vessels. The study is called thermography.

Radioactive substances that have been injected into the body can be followed in their travels by special scanning machines. Again, pictures can be made that show up diseased or damaged organs inside the body. (*See* RADIOISOTOPE.)

In all these techniques, computers can be used to help produce clear pictures. Computers are widely used in hospitals to aid diagnosis. Some computer-controlled machines perform a series of chemical tests on blood samples and print out the results.

Other instruments may be used to record the electrical activity of the body's organs. The working of the heart is recorded by means of an electrocardiogram. Brain waves are recorded by an electroencephalogram. The readings may be in the form of wave tracings on paper strips or as traces on a screen.

Optical instruments called endoscopes are used to look inside the body directly. They are narrow tubes with lenses and lights. A gastroscope is used to examine the inside of the stomach. A bronchoscope is used to examine the air passages and lungs from inside. These are both endoscopes. Many endoscopes now use fine optical fibers to transmit light. (*See* FIBER OPTICS.)

Machines for treatment One of the earliest life-saving machines was the iron lung. This aids the breathing of someone whose chest muscles are paralyzed. It has an airtight chamber to enclose the patient's trunk. By altering the pressure inside the chamber, the patient is helped to breathe in and out.

During operations on the heart, a heart-lung machine is often used. This takes over the function of the patient's heart and lungs. The surgeon is able to stop the heart safely to perform surgery on it. Heart-assist devices and artificial pacemakers help the heart to pump regularly if it is diseased or damaged. Artificial valves may be sewn into the heart to replace ones that do not work properly. Continual progress is being made in developing artificial hearts, the first of which was implanted in a human being in 1982.

Another very important machine is the artificial kidney machine. It saves the lives of thousands of patients whose kidneys are damaged. The patient is "plugged in" to the machine. His blood is returned without the waste material that would otherwise accumulate and poison him. A kidney machine is generally used for several hours twice a week.

Making artificial limbs and joints is an important medical engineering specialty. New hip joints are made from plastic and metal. They are implanted to replace joints worn out and diseased. Other joints, such as the knee, may also be replaced. Whole artificial limbs may be worked by electric motors. They are controlled by electric signals picked up from the healthy nerves and muscles of the stump. Lifelike artificial hands with a good range of movements have been developed. They are constantly being improved. (*See* BIOPHYSICS.) D.M.H.W./J.J.F.

MEDICINE (med′ ə sən) Medicine is the science of preventing and treating disease. It involves a thorough understanding of the body's structure and the ways in which its working can go wrong. It involves knowledge of the causes of disease and study of the results of all forms of treatment.

There are two main types of medical specialist. Surgeons deal with cases where it is necessary to cut into the body to undertake treatment. (*See* SURGERY.) Physicians deal with cases that can be treated without surgery.

There are many branches of medicine. Psychiatry deals with mental disorders. Preventive medicine deals with removing the causes of disease. Pathology deals with the changes in the tissues of the body that diseases cause. Gynecology is the study of women's diseases, and obstetrics is concerned with childbirth. Anesthesiologists are experts in drugs to relieve pain and in producing unconsciousness during operations. Radiologists are concerned with the effects of radiation on the body. These are only a few of the specialized branches of medicine.

Diagnosis Diagnosis is finding out the cause of a person's illness. Physicians find out the cause by listening to the patients' accounts of what they find wrong with themselves and then examining the patients. The changes that the patients report are called symptoms. Things that physicians notice are wrong are called signs. Together, the signs and symptoms will point to a possible cause, or causes, for the illness.

To confirm their diagnoses, physicians may ask for special tests to be carried out on patients. They may ask radiologists to examine X rays of parts of the body. They may study samples of cells taken from an organ. They may examine body fluids such as the urine, blood, or spinal fluid to find out if bacteria are present. Many machines and devices are available to aid physicians. The electrocardiogram tells them about the electrical activity of the heart. The electroencephalogram gives them a picture of the electrical changes in the brain. (*See* MEDICAL ENGINEERING.) Physicians can call upon many different specialists to help them reach a correct diagnosis.

Treatment The aim of treatment is to remove the cause of the illness that has been diagnosed and to help the patient overcome whatever is wrong. Surgeons may be able to cut out a diseased part of the body. They may remove a tumor or an ulcer. They may even replace a faulty heart valve. Physicians will often use drugs to cure the patient. Antibiotics can be used to conquer infections caused by bacteria or fungi. Other drugs may be used to correct upsets of the body's chemistry.

Another term for treatment is therapy. Different kinds of therapy have their own names. Radiotherapy is the use of X rays or other radiation to cure disease. Chemotherapy is the use of drugs. Psychotherapy is the treatment of mental disorders. Physical therapy is treatment of disease by means of water, light, heat, sound, electricity, massage, or exercise. It is the doctor's responsibility to decide what the best form of therapy is for the patient.

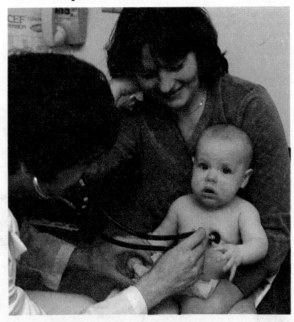

A periodic physical examination is one of the best ways to diagnose and prevent illnesses.

History Primitive people did not understand disease. Illnesses were mysterious; they were regarded as evil. Treatment consisted of magic and ritual that was based on superstition. Witch doctors or medicine men were often part of primitive cultures. Besides their superstitions, these early doctors often used herbal medicines to cure some ailments.

By about 3000 B.C., Mesopotamian physicians had recorded a long list of effective herbs and drugs. By 2800 B.C., the Chinese had a similar record. The Egyptians took the first steps toward a controlled, scientific practice of medicine. From 3000 to 1000 B.C., they developed ways to measure the pulse, and they understood how blood circulates. They knew the importance of changes in body temperature, used splints for broken bones, prescribed a wide variety of drugs, and practiced relatively advanced surgical techniques.

The Greeks continued the scientific approach to medicine. They learned how bodies functioned by examining or dissecting dead bodies. The Greek teacher Hippocrates recorded much of what was learned, and composed the first standard of professional ethics for those who practiced medicine.

The Romans recorded their medical knowledge. When the Roman Empire fell, the information was preserved by the Arabs. They added to it as they conquered other lands.

During the Middle Ages, the practice of medicine did not progress; rather, it declined. It was not until the Renaissance that scientific medical practice began again, using experimentation, observation, reason, and logic.

Tremendous progress was made in medicine from 1700 to 1900. Among other things, it was due to the inventions of the microscope, thermometer, and stethoscope; the discovery of anesthesia and X rays; and the formulation of the principles of antiseptic surgery. By 1900, doctors also knew about immunization and sanitation for the prevention of illness. In the 20th century, development of antibiotics has conquered many infectious diseases, and the new science of medical engineering has produced such wonders as the artificial heart. *See also* DENTISTRY; MENTAL HEALTH; PATHOLOGY; VETERINARY MEDICINE.

D.M.H.W./J.J.F.

Modern equipment has made preventative medicine much more effective.

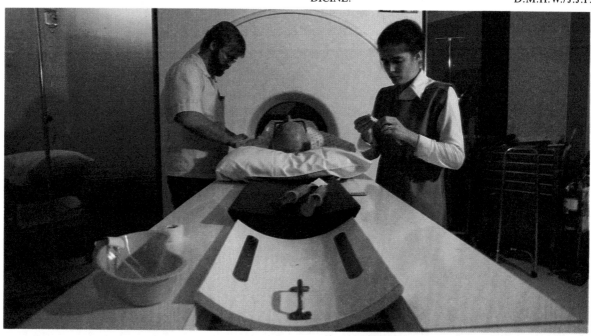

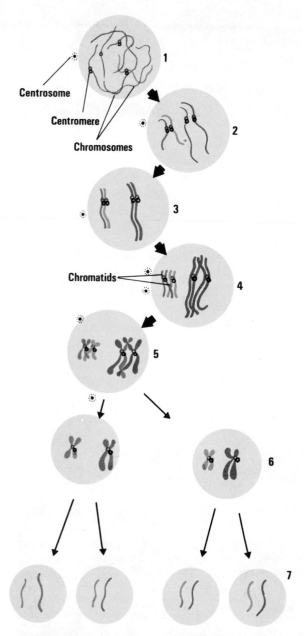

Centrosome

Centromere

Chromosomes

Chromatids

Meiosis 1. Chromosomes are long and threadlike. 2. As meiosis begins, the chromosome pairs line up with the centromeres along the midline of the nucleus. 3. The chromosomes get shorter. 4. Each chromosome doubles to form a pair of chromatids which remain joined at the centromeres. 5. As the chromatids continue to become shorter, there may be some crossing-over, or exchange of genetic material. 6. The chromsomes move to opposite ends of the cell and the cell splits in two. 7. Each of these cells then splits again, but without doubling the chromosomes. As a result there are four daughter cells.

MEIOSIS (mī ō′ səs) Meiosis is the process whereby a cell doubles its chromosomes once and then divides twice to produce four "daughter" cells. Each of these daughter cells has half the number of chromosomes of the parent cell. (*See* CHROMOSOME.) Meiosis is characteristic of sex cells in both plants and animals. (*See* GAMETE.)

Chromosomes exist in pairs in the nucleus of a cell. When meiosis begins, the chromosomes line up in pairs along the mid-line of the nucleus. Each chromosome then doubles, or forms another one like itself. These duplicated chromosomes are now called chromatids. It is at this stage—when the chromosomes have doubled to form chromatids—that there may be some crossing-over, or exchange of genetic material. over, or exchange of genetic material. (*See* HEREDITARY.) The membrane around the nucleus then disappears and a spindle of protein fibers forms, one fiber attached to each chromosome. The fibers then pull the chromosomes (actually, pairs of chromatids) to opposite ends of the cell. A nuclear membrane forms around each group of chromatid pairs, and the cell divides in two. Each of these cells has the normal number of chromosomes. This first part of meiosis is very similar to mitosis, the other type of cell division. (*See* MITOSIS.)

Each of these two new cells then divides again. This time, however, the chromosomes are not doubled. The chromatid pairs split, one from each pair going to the new cell. As a result, each of these four daughter cells has half the normal number of chromosomes of the original parent cell. A gamete is a cell with half the normal number of chromosomes. During sexual reproduction, a male gamete combines with a female gamete to produce a zygote with the full number of chromosomes. Thus, the zygote gets half of its chromosomes from one parent and half from the other parent. *See also* FERTILIZATION; REPRODUCTION.

A.J.C./E.R.L.

MELON (mel′ ən) Melon is the fruit of several plants belonging to the gourd family

Cucurbitaceae. The plants have trailing vines that attach themselves to objects. They attach by means of tendrils. Tendrils are modified leaves resembling wire coils.

Melons are round to oblong in shape. They range from 2.5 cm [1 in] to more than 30 cm [12 in] across. They are tan, yellow, green, or pink in color.

Cantaloupe, muskmelon, honeydew, casaba, and watermelon are all popular types of melon. Melons are an ancient fruit. Watermelons were cultivated by the ancient Egyptians in the 14th and 13th centuries B.C. *See also* GOURD FAMILY. J.M.C./M.H.S.

MELTING POINT (mel' ting point) The melting point of a substance is the temperature at which it turns from a solid into a liquid. Melting points vary from one substance to another. They are sometimes used to test the purity of a material. An impure material has a different melting point from a pure one. The melting point of a substance varies with the pressure. For this reason, melting points are usually given for a pressure of one atmosphere. M.E./A.D.

MEMBRANE (mem' brān') In biology, there are two main types of membranes: cellular membranes and body membranes. A cellular membrane is part of a cell. It may enclose the cell, or it may enclose or be part of a structure within the cell. A body membrane is made up of cells. It is a thin sheet of tissue that covers, lines, separates, or connects body structures.

Cellular membranes All cells are enclosed by a cell membrane, which is also called a plasma membrane. (*See* CELL.) Many cells also have internal structures, or organelles, that are enclosed in membranes. Some organelles, such as mitochondria, Golgi bodies, and endoplasmic reticulum, are made of folds of membrane. In some cells, such as those of bacteria and plants, the cell membrane is sur-

MELTING POINTS OF NONMETALLIC ELEMENTS AND SOME COMMON COMPOUNDS					
Substance	°C	°F	Substance	°C	°F
Hydrazine	2	36	Silver chloride	455	851
Nitrobenzene	6	43	Cupric chloride	498	928
Cyclohexane	6	43	Silver iodide	558	1036
Sulfuric acid	11	52	Barium nitrate	592	1098
Sulfur trioxide	17	63	Potassium cyanide	635	1175
Nitrogen pentoxide	32	90	Manganese chloride	650	1202
Phenol	41	106	Potassium iodide	685	1265
Phosphorus (white)	44	111	Magnesium chloride	714	1317
Ferrous sulfate	64	147	Potassium bromide	735	1355
Copper sulfate	110	230	Calcium chloride	782	1440
Iodine	114	237	Sodium chloride	808	1486
Sulfur (monoclinic)	119	246	Arsenic (under pressure)	817	1503
Ammonium nitrate	170	338	Sodium carbonate	858	1576
Selenium	217	423	Lead monoxide	886	1627
Astatine	302	576	Potassium carbonate	896	1645
Mercuric chloride	277	531	Barium chloride	963	1765
Ferric chloride	304	579	Cuprous oxide	1234	2253
Sodium hydroxide	319	606	Silicon	1410	2570
Potassium nitrate	337	639	Ferric oxide	1560	2840
Potassium chlorate	368	694	Silicon dioxide (quartz)	1610	2930
Potassium hydroxide	361	682	Boron	2300	4172
Cuprous chloride	430	806	Calcium oxide	2600	4712
Silver bromide	430	806	Carbon (diamond)	3550	6422

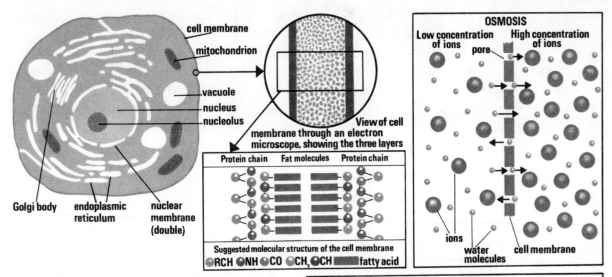

View of cell membrane through an electron microscope, showing the three layers

Suggested molecular structure of the cell membrane

OSMOSIS

ACTIVE TRANSPORT

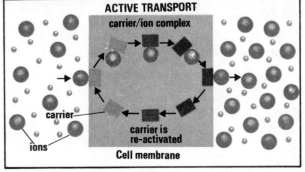

Substances must be able to pass through the cell membrane. Water passes into the cell by osmosis, in which water molecules diffuse through the pores in the cell membrane from a region of low concentration of ions to a region of high concentration. Ions are generally too large to pass through the pores. They are passed into the cell by active transport. A "carrier" molecule picks up the ion and transfers it across the membrane. In doing so the carrier molecule loses energy and has to be reactivated before it can be used again.

rounded by a cell wall. The cell wall protects, strengthens, and adds form to the cell. Bacterial cells, while lacking organelles such as a nucleus and mitochondria, have other organelles called mesosomes. The function of these membrane-enclosed mesosomes is uncertain. In bacterial cells some structures, such as RNA and ribosomes, are attached directly to the cell membrane.

Cellular membranes are made of a double layer of lipids sandwiched between two layers of protein. They also contain small amounts of carbohydrates and RNA. Some, if not all, cellular membranes have the ability to carry an electrical charge. This is due to the presence of ions (charged atoms) on both sides of the membrane. (*See* IONS AND IONIZATION.) This is important to the functioning of the cell. In nerve cells, it is needed to transmit nerve signals. (*See* NERVE CELL.)

Cellular membranes are vital to the life of

a cell. The cell membrane separates the cell from its environment. It allows some substances, such as food and oxygen, to enter the cell. It allows other substances, such as carbon dioxide and metabolic wastes, to leave the cell. It keeps some substances out of the cell altogether. Because these membranes are selective, they are said to be semipermeable.

All membranes in the cell are semipermeable. This means these membranes allow more substances through at some times than at others. Water usually moves through a membrane by osmosis. (*See* OSMOSIS.) The amount of water that passes through the membrane depends on osmotic pressure and hydrostatic pressure. (*See* HYDROSTATICS.)

Solid particles may move through the membrane in one of three ways. Some particles diffuse through the membrane in an attempt to establish a balance, or equilibrium, on both sides of the membrane. (*See* DIFFUSION.)

Small particles and ions may be carried across the membrane by active transport. Active transport is related to the electrical charge on the membrane, and requires energy from the cell. Larger particles and molecules are sometimes moved across a membrane by pinocytosis. In pinocytosis, part of the membrane surrounds a particle, forming a vacuole around the particle. (*See* VACUOLE.) Pinocytosis also requires energy from the cell.

Body membranes   There are three types of body membranes: fibrous, mucous, and serous. All are thin sheets of tissue made up of various types of specialized cells.

Fibrous membranes are made of tough connective tissue. (*See* CONNECTIVE TISSUE.) They strengthen and support many body structures. The periosteum is a fibrous membrane that covers the bones. The dura mater is the membrane that lines the inner surface of the skull.

Mucous membranes line organs and the body cavities that open to the outside. They contain special glands that secrete a clear, sticky fluid called mucus. Mucous membranes are found in the mouth, nose, throat, alimentary canal, trachea, lungs, reproductive system, eyelids, and inner ear.

Serous membranes line body cavities that do not open to the outside, and contain cells which secrete a watery fluid to keep them moist. This fluid also keeps the membranes from sticking to each other or to other organs. The pleura is a serous membrane that lines the lung cavities. The peritoneum lines the abdominal cavity. The synovial membrane lines the joints between bones. It produces a fluid called synovial fluid which lubricates the joints.   A.J.C./E.R.L.

MENDEL, GREGOR (1822–1884) Gregor Mendel (men′ dəl) was an Austrian monk. He studied science at the University of Vienna. Then he returned to his monastery at Brünn (Brno) and taught at the school there.

Mendel grew plants in his monastery garden. He used them to make his careful experiments in genetics. His most famous experiments were done with peas. He found that heredity followed a simple set of mathematical rules. Mendel interpreted this as meaning that there were tiny particles in living cells that controlled heredity. We now call these particles genes.

Mendel's discoveries were not noticed by other scientists while he was alive. They were rediscovered by other scientists in 1900. Today we know that the laws of heredity are more complicated than Mendel thought. But his basic ideas still hold true. *See also* GENE; GENETICS; MORGAN, THOMAS HUNT.

C.M./D.G.F.

Gregor Mendel

MENDELEEV, DMITRI (1834–1907) Dmitri Mendeleev (men′ də lā′ ef) was a Russian chemist. He was born at Tobolsk and studied and worked at St. Petersburg (Leningrad) University.

Mendeleev worked out a way of classifying chemical elements. It is called the periodic table. He used the atomic weights and valences of elements to arrange them in a special order. There were some gaps in Mendeleev's table. He was so sure that his arrangement was correct that he said that the missing elements would one day be discovered. Three new elements, gallium, scandium, and germanium, fitted perfectly into the table when they were later discovered. We still use the periodic table today. It is very useful in helping us to understand and predict the way elements behave. *See also* ELEMENT.

C.M./D.G.F.

Dmitri Mendeleev

MENDELEVIUM (men′ də lē′ vē əm) Mendelevium (Md) is a radioactive metallic element. Its atomic number is 101. Only very small amounts of the metal have been produced so far. Its melting and boiling points have not yet been measured.

Mendelevium does not occur in nature. It was first made by a team of scientists headed by the American physicist Glenn T. Seaborg in 1955. They obtained the metal by bombarding an isotope of einsteinium with alpha particles. Four isotopes of mendelevium have so far been discovered. (*See* ISOTOPE.) The longest-lived isotope decays by half in two months. No uses have yet been discovered for the metal. *See also* RADIOACTIVITY; TRANSURANIC ELEMENT.

M.E./J.R.W.

MENISCUS (mə nis′ kəs) Suppose that a liquid is placed in a container. The surface of the liquid becomes curved near the walls of the container. This curved surface is called the meniscus. The meniscus can be either concave or convex. If the surface curves upward away from the liquid, the meniscus is convex. If it curves downward towards the liquid, it is concave. If the meniscus is concave, the liquid is said to wet the container. In glass containers, water and alcohol have concave surfaces. Therefore they wet the container. Mercury has a convex meniscus and does not wet glassware.

The molecules in a liquid are attracted to each other. They are also attracted to the molecules in the container. Sometimes the molecules in the liquid are more attracted to the molecules in the container than to each other. The liquid is then pulled a little way up the side of the container because of this attraction. A concave meniscus forms. If the molecules in the liquid are more attracted to each other, the opposite happens. A convex meniscus forms.

The shape of the meniscus depends on what the container is made of. The molecules in a liquid are attracted by different amounts to different molecules.

M.E./R.W.L.

MENSTRUAL CYCLE (men′ strəl sī′ kəl) When a girl is old enough to have a baby, her reproductive system begins to work. This usually happens between the ages of 11 and 16. First an egg (ovum) becomes ripe in the ovary. At the same time, the uterus gets ready in case the egg is fertilized. Fertilized eggs grow into babies in the uterus. If the egg is not fertilized, it breaks down and the material in the uterus passes out of the body. This happens about every four weeks and is called the menstrual cycle, from the Latin word for month. It is not always exactly four weeks. Sometimes the cycle happens over three or even six weeks.

When the uterus is getting ready for the egg, its lining, or endometrium thickens and becomes cushiony. Its blood supply increases. This is caused by a hormone (estrogen) which is released by the ovaries. About two weeks later, a ripe egg is released from one of the ovaries. This is called ovulation. The part of the ovary where the egg comes from secretes another hormone, called progesterone. This also helps to prepare the uterus. If the egg is fertilized, it settles in the soft lining of the uterus and starts to grow.

If the egg is not fertilized, the ovaries stop making estrogen and progesterone for a short time. This allows the uterus to get rid of its contents and prepare itself to receive the next egg. The thick lining is cast off and passes through the vagina and out of the body. Every month some blood and waste cells flow from the vagina. This is called menstruation, or the menstrual period. It usually lasts between four and six days. Then the cycle starts again, with ovulation taking place two weeks after the start of menstruation. The amount of blood lost at menstruation is really very small. It is mostly the blood that is in the lining as it is shed. When a woman is about 45, she stops menstruating. There are no more eggs released and she no longer has menstrual periods. The time when this happens is called the menopause. C.M./J.J.F.

MENSURATION (men′ sə rā′ shən) Mensuration is a branch of mathematics that studies measurement. In mensuration, the lengths of lines and the areas and volumes of different shapes are calculated. This is done by using geometry, trigonometry, and other fields of mathematics. (*See* GEOMETRY; TRIGONOMETRY.) Simple formulas for areas and volumes were known to the ancient Greeks about 2,500 years ago. M.E./S.P.A.

Simple areas can be calculated from the area of a circle and the area of a rectangle.

MENTAL HEALTH

A person's body can be healthy or sick, and so can the mind. Mental illness means sickness of the mind. Mentally ill persons are sick people, just as persons suffering from a bad cold or heart disease are sick people. Like other sick persons, the mentally ill need special treatment. Mental health (ment′ əl helth) includes the prevention of mental and emotional disorders and the detection, treatment, and rehabilitation (restoring of mental health) of the mentally ill. Mental health is also concerned with promoting a sense of mental well-being.

About 200 years ago, doctors began to realize that people with mental disorders were sick. Doctors started to study mental illness and to try to treat it, as they did physical illnesses. During the late 1800s, Sigmund Freud worked out his psychoanalytic theory. This theory states that unconscious ideas can affect health. (*See* FREUD, SIGMUND.)

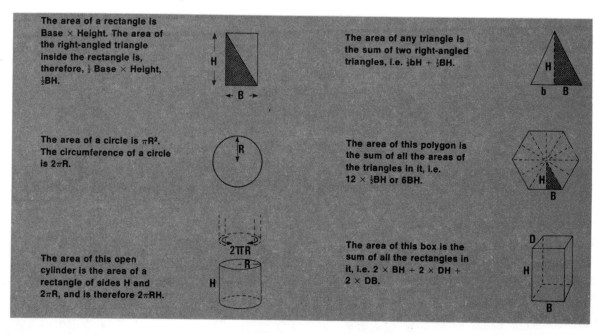

The area of a rectangle is Base × Height. The area of the right-angled triangle inside the rectangle is, therefore, ½ Base × Height, ½BH.

The area of any triangle is the sum of two right-angled triangles, i.e. ½bH + ½BH.

The area of a circle is πR^2. The circumference of a circle is $2\pi R$.

The area of this polygon is the sum of all the areas of the triangles in it, i.e. 12 × ½BH or 6BH.

The area of this open cylinder is the area of a rectangle of sides H and $2\pi R$, and is therefore $2\pi RH$.

The area of this box is the sum of all the rectangles in it, i.e. 2 × BH + 2 × DH + 2 × DB.

Treatment of mental illness is better now than ever before. But study of this illness is relatively new. Not much is known about it.

Types of mental illness Most doctors divide mental illness into two types—organic and functional. Organic mental illness is caused by damage to the brain. The cause can be a high fever, an accident, or a change in the amount of hormones the body produces. (*See* HORMONE.) Certain kinds of organic mental disorders are treated not as mental illness but as diseases of the nervous system. These include epilepsy, cerebral palsy, and Parkinson's disease. Other organic mental disorders are caused by brain injury. Amnesia is the loss of memory. Aphasia is a disorder of thought and communication.

Most mental illnesses are functional disorders. In a functional disorder, a person's mind is ill without any apparent damage to the brain. In other words, experts cannot find damage to the brain, but the mind does not work properly. The causes of functional mental illness are not very well understood. It is possible that if a child does not have the proper love and attention he or she could show signs of mental illness. But this is not always true. Experts also say that a shocking experience, such as a terrible automobile accident, may cause mental illness. This is not always true, either. Much research must still be done to find out what the causes of many functional disorders are.

Functional disorders fall under two main groups. The most common one is neurosis. Neurosis is a mild emotional disorder. A neurotic person's thoughts or actions can upset his relations with other people or make him unhappy. Though neurosis reduces a person's ability to live happily, the person does not seriously lose a sense of reality. There are several common types of neuroses. Certain symptoms of all kinds of neuroses may appear in a neurotic person, or various mixtures of such symptoms may occur. Anxiety neurosis may lead to abnormal fear or dread of death or of certain places or people. This fear, in some cases called a phobia, could seriously disturb the person's life. Common examples are claustrophobia, the fear of closed-in spaces, and acrophobia, the fear of heights. People with obsessive and compulsive neuroses have repeated urges to perform certain acts. They may spend much of their time performing the same acts over and over again. Hysteria has physical symptoms, such as paralysis, without an apparent physical cause. Character neuroses include passiveness, aggressiveness, moodiness, and elation.

The second type of functional disorders of mental illness is psychosis. A neurotic person knows what is real and what is not. But a psychotic person may think imaginary people or events are real. In manic-depressive psychosis, the patient may feel excited and elated (mania) or may be miserable, gloomy, and without hope (depression). His or her mood may swing between one state and the other. The fact that many cases of manic-depressive psychosis can be cured or relieved with drugs suggests that chemical changes in the brain may be a major cause. But depression may also be a psychological reaction to a shock, such as the death of a close friend. In schizophrenia, the other main type of psychosis, a person's whole mind and personality become disrupted. Schizophrenia means a shattering of the mind. The patient's intelligence may remain normal, but his or her emotions do not fit real-life situations. Schizophrenia does not mean that the patient has more than one personality. In catatonic schizophrenia, a person may become completely inactive and immobile. He or she may not seem to respond to reality. In hebephrenic schizophrenia, a person talks and behaves in a strange manner. He or she may behave childishly. Such patients suffer from rapid mental deterioration (decay). People with paranoid schizophrenia believe that other persons persecute them, and they behave accordingly. People who suffer from simple schizophrenia are emotionally dull, withdrawn, and often stay by themselves. They show no strange symptoms, and often go along for some time before their illness is detected. Their emotions slowly diminish (become less and less strong).

New evidence suggests that schizophrenia may be either organic or functional. Doctors now believe that an inherited component, either biochemical or neurological, can increase a person's chances of becoming schizophrenic.

Paranoia, an illness that many doctors consider a type of schizophrenia, may also be present separately. Such persons show megalomania, or an exaggerated degree of self-love. They believe that other people act mean toward them. Unlike the paranoid schizophrenics, persons suffering from paranoia seem to be able to behave properly.

Treatment of mental illness Experts have many different ideas about how to treat mental illness. Some medical doctors specialize in mental illnesses. These people are called psychiatrists. For the most part, they use psychotherapy. In psychotherapy, the psychiatrist listens to the patients talk about their troubles and then helps the patients to understand what is disturbing them. Psychoanalysis is a special form of this method. Other types of psychotherapy include group therapy, in which a group of patients try to help each other. Another type is behavior therapy, which uses methods such as conditioning to teach the patients to overcome their problems. (*See* LEARNING AND MEMORY.) Medical techniques, such as drugs and electroshock therapy, are also used by psychiatrists to treat mental illnesses. Important drugs used for the physical treatment of mental illnesses include antidepressants, which fight depression, tranquilizers, which calm agitated and anxious patients (including many schizophrenics), and sedatives, which help a person to sleep.

A diet containing the element lithium has been found to help many causes of depression. In shock therapy, a small electric current is passed through part of the brain as a treatment for depression.

Most doctors no longer put special emphasis on any one aspect of human life as leading to mental illness. They recognize many factors that contribute to mental illness. All these factors are considered in treating the patients. The experts realize that there are other factors which, when known, may lead to further improvements and progress in the treatment of mental illness.   J.J.A./J.J.F.

MENTHOL (men′ thȯl) Menthol is a colorless crystalline substance with the chemical formula $C_{10}H_{20}O$. Its crystals melt at 42°C [108°F].

Menthol is found in peppermint plants. It can be extracted from these plants or made artificially. Its refreshing odor and taste cause it to be used in the making of some perfumes and as a flavoring in some toothpastes and candies.

Because menthol is a mild painkiller, it is used in analgesics to numb the skin. (*See* ANALGESIC.) It is also contained in some drugs useful for the treatment of coughs and the common cold.   M.E./J.M.

MERCURY (mәr′ kyә rē) Mercury is the planet closest to the sun. Mercury has a diameter of 4,990 km [3,100 mi], which makes it the second smallest known planet of the solar system. Mercury averages 57.9 million km [36 million mi] from the sun. It takes the planet only 88 earth-days to make a complete orbit around the sun.

It takes Mercury 59 earth-days to make a complete rotation on its axis. Until 1965, astronomers thought that the time it took Mercury to go around the sun was the same as its rotation period. If this was true, one side of Mercury would always face the sun, and the other side would always be dark. Astronomers used radar to determine that Mercury's rotation period is 29 days less than its year. This means that both sides of Mercury receive light from the sun.

The landscape of Mercury is similar to that of the earth's moon. Mercury has craters, cliffs, and broad plains. Astronomers think that silicate rocks form a thin layer on the planet. The interior of Mercury may contain a large iron-nickel core.

Until a few years ago, Mercury was not thought to have an atmosphere. However, the newer measurements of its surface temperatures have led scientists to different conclusions. Daytime temperatures reach about 427°C [800°F], and night temperatures only go down to about 21°C [70°F]. The night temperatures are much warmer than predicted, and indicate that there is some kind of atmosphere.

Because of its nearness to the sun and its small size, Mercury is difficult to see without a telescope. Every 3 to 13 years, Mercury passes between the sun and the earth. When this happens, Mercury is said to be in transit, and the planet appears as a black spot against the sun. Astronomers gain valuable knowledge about Mercury during these transit periods.

In 1974, the American space probe

Cinnabar is an ore of mercury.

Mariner X flew within 740 km [460 mi] of Mercury. Mariner X took many photographs of Mercury and determined that the planet has a magnetic field. (*See* MAGNETISM.) Mariner X also studied Venus, thus becoming the first space probe to study two planets. *See also* EXOBIOLOGY; PLANET.   J.M.C./C.R.

MERCURY (mər′ kyə rē) Mercury (Hg) is a metallic element. It is the only metal that is a liquid at normal temperatures. The atomic number of mercury is 80 and its atomic weight is 200.59. Mercury melts at −39°C [−38°F] and boils at 359°C [678°F]. The relative density of mercury is 13.5.

Mercury has been known since ancient times. Its symbol, Hg, comes from its Latin name, *hydrargyrus*, which means ''water silver.'' Mercury is a relatively unreactive metal and is sometimes found uncombined in nature. Most mercury, though, occurs as mercuric sulfide in the mineral cinnabar. To extract the mercury, the mineral is heated, sometimes with lime. The mercuric sulfide decomposes and mercury vapor is given off. The mercury is collected and cooled to obtain liquid mercury.

Mercury and its compounds have many different uses. Liquid mercury is used in barometers and thermometers. Mercury-vapor lamps are used as street lamps, sunlamps, and fluorescent lamps. In these lamps, an electric current is passed through mercury vapor. The vapor gives off a bright blue-white light and ultraviolet rays. Mercury forms alloys with other metals. These alloys are called amalgams. (*See* AMALGAM.) Amalgams are used for filling teeth in dentistry. They are also used in industry.

Mercury forms two series of compounds. In one series, mercury has a valence of one. (*See* VALENCE.) They are called mercury (I), or mercurous, compounds. The other series of compounds has mercury with a valence of two. They are called mercury (II), or mercuric, compounds. Mercury (I) chloride, or calomel, is used in medicine. Mercury (II) chloride is a strong antiseptic and preservative. It is also known as corrosive sublimate. The red pigment vermillion consists of mercury (II) chloride. Both mercury and its compounds are very poisonous and should be handled with great care. M.E./J.R.W.

MERGANSER (mər gan′ sər) Merganser is the name for a group of fish-eating ducks. The merganser's bill is hooked at the tip and notched at the edges. Because of this bill, the merganser is frequently called a sawbill or a sheldrake. Mergansers are found in many different parts of the world. Mergansers have tufts of feathers that form a crest on their heads. The male's feathers are black and white. The female's are grayish brown.

The common merganser (*Mergus merganser*), red-breasted merganser (*Mergus serrator*), and hooded merganser (*Lophodytes cucullatus*) are found throughout North America. The common merganser has a shiny, greenish black head and neck. The red-breasted merganser has a rusty-red breast. The hooded merganser has a black and white head crest. *See also* DUCK. J.J.A./L.L.S.

MERISTEM (mer′ ə stem′) Meristem is plant tissue which is made up of cells that are actively dividing and growing. Meristem

cells are usually small and almost cube-shaped. They have dense cytoplasm and few, if any, vacuoles. (*See* CYTOPLASM; VACUOLE.)

Meristem is found in the growing regions of plants. Apical meristem is found in the tips of roots and shoots. It is sometimes called primary meristem because it causes an increase in length. Lateral meristem is found along the sides of roots and shoots. (*See* CAMBIUM.) Lateral meristem forms the vascular tissues of the plant. It is sometimes called secondary meristem because it causes an increase in width. Intercalary meristem is found in the internodes. Internodes are the spaces along a stem between the nodes, or points of leaf attachment. Intercalary meristem is frequently temporary. It is characteristic of monocotyledons such as the grasses. If a plant is injured, meristem develops in the injured area. It produces many cells which help heal the wound. *See also* GROWTH; MITOSIS.

A.J.C./M.H.S.

Below, cross sections of the tip of a stem and a root tip. In both cases the process of development, or differentiation, starts with a group of very simple cells, usually called the promeristem. These cells divide and, after division, some of the resulting cells develop into more complex cells. As the stem or root grows, these cells are left behind the tip and develop further into fully differentiated tissues. The meristem of the young plant gives rise to all the plant's tissues.

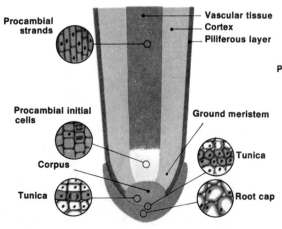

ROOT APEX, VERTICAL SECTION

Procambial strands — Vascular tissue — Cortex — Piliferous layer — Procambial initial cells — Ground meristem — Corpus — Tunica — Tunica — Root cap

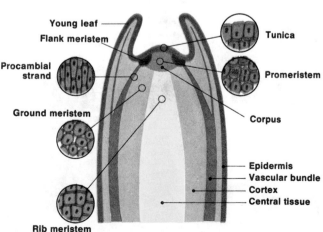

STEM APEX, VERTICAL SECTION

Young leaf — Flank meristem — Procambial strand — Ground meristem — Rib meristem — Tunica — Promeristem — Corpus — Epidermis — Vascular bundle — Cortex — Central tissue

MESA (mā′ sə) A mesa is a flat-topped, steep-sided land formation. Mesas are the leftovers of large plateaus which have been worn away by erosion. A mesa remains because it is capped with hard rock that does not erode easily.

Mesas are found in the semi-arid regions of the western and southwestern United States. They are often covered with grass or scrubby vegetation. The word *mesa* means table in Spanish. A small mesa is called a butte. *See also* EROSION.   J.M.C./W.R.S.

Mesas are named after the Spanish word for table.

MESON (mez′ än′) Mesons are a group of elementary particles. They are all unstable and quickly break down into other particles. They can be made by colliding two elementary particles together. This is done in large machines called particle accelerators. (*See* ACCELERATOR, PARTICLE.) When two particles collide, they sometimes destroy themselves and form other particles. Very often, mesons are formed. They have masses between those of an electron and a proton.

Mesons are responsible for strong interactions in the nucleus of an atom. The most important mesons are the pi mesons or pions. They are believed to be responsible for the force that binds the nucleus of an atom together. (*See* NUCLEUS, ATOMIC.) The nucleus contains two particles, called protons and neutrons. Some scientists believe these particles exchange pions with each other. This causes the particles in the nucleus to bind together very strongly. *See also* PARTICLE PHYSICS.   M.E./J.T.

MESOZOIC ERA (mez′ ə zō′ ik ir′ ə) The Mesozoic era began about 225 million years ago and ended about 65 million years ago. It includes the Triassic, Jurassic, and Cretaceous periods.

The first part of the Mesozoic era is the Triassic period. During this time, conifers became plentiful. The first dinosaurs, turtles,

A Mesozoic scene. 1. Pteranodon, a flying reptile. 2. Rhamphoryncus, a tailed flying reptile. 3. A primitive bird. 4. Camptosaurus. 5. Triconodon, an early mammal. 6. A tortoise. 7. Stegosaurus, an armor-plated dinosaur. 8. Diplodocus. 9. Brontosaurus. 10. Conifers. 11. Cycads. 12. Bennetitales. 13. Ferns.

and crocodiles appeared on earth. Fish similar to those of today swam in the water.

The middle section of the Mesozoic era is called the Jurassic period. Dinosaurs reached their largest size at that time. Birds and primitive land mammals appeared.

The Cretaceous period is the last part of the Mesozoic era. Flowering plants spread rapidly during the Cretaceous period. Armored and horned dinosaurs were common. By the end of the Mesozoic era, dinosaurs had become extinct. *See also* DINOSAUR; GEOLOGICAL TIME SCALE. J.M.C./W.R.S.

METABOLISM (mə tab′ ə liz′ əm) Metabolism is the whole system of chemical reactions that take place in the cells of living organisms. It may involve producing food by photosynthesis or changing food into energy and living tissue. There are two types of metabolism: catabolism and anabolism. Catabolism, or destructive metabolism, involves the breaking down of complex food particles to release energy. This energy is used to heat the body, to allow muscles and nerves to function properly, and to allow anabolism. Anabolism, or constructive metabolism, involves building up cells and tissues and repairing or replacing worn-out tissues.

Metabolism is a constant process. If metabolism were to stop, an organism would die. The basal metabolic rate (BMR) is the rate of metabolism of a resting organism. It is the rate at which the body uses food to produce energy. The BMR is related to many factors such as a person's sex, age, and weight. It is controlled mainly by thyroxine. Thyroxine is a hormone released by the thyroid gland. (*See* HORMONE.) Scientists are able to measure a person's BMR by means of a special blood test, or by measuring the amount of oxygen used while a person is at rest. A low BMR may indicate hypothyroidism, a condition in which the thyroid releases too little thyroxine. A person with a low BMR is usually over-weight, tired, and sluggish. A high BMR may indicate hyperthyroidism, a condition in which the thyroid releases too much thyroxine. A person with a high BMR is usually underweight, nervous, and anxious. Certain drugs have an effect on a person's metabolic rate. Amphetamines increase the rate of metabolism while barbiturates decrease the rate of metabolism.

Any disease that is due to abnormal body chemistry is called a metabolic disorder. Some metabolic disorders, such as diabetes, Addison's disease, and certain mental diseases, develop after birth. Other metabolic disorders, such as albinism and sickle cell anemia, are inherited and are established before birth. (*See* HEREDITY.) *See also* KREBS CYCLE. A.J.C./E.R.L.

METAL AND METALLURGY Most metals (met′ əlz) are heavy, shiny solids. They are good conductors of heat and electricity. (*See* CONDUCTION OF ELECTRICITY; CONDUCTION, HEAT.) Most of the chemical elements are metals. Almost all metals are solids at normal (room) temperatures. A few metals are very light. For example, lithium, sodium, and potassium are all lighter than water.

All matter is made up of atoms. (*See* ATOM.) Atoms have a central core called a nucleus with a number of electrons moving around it. Some of these electrons are closer to the nucleus than others. The outermost electrons are usually held only weakly to the atom. It is quite easy for them to transfer themselves to other atoms. This is how atoms bind together to form molecules. In a metal, the outermost electrons are not held by any atom in particular. They can move freely throughout the whole of the metal. An electric current is a flow of electrons. If an electric current can flow easily through a material, the material is said to conduct electricity. Since a metal contains free electrons, it can easily conduct electricity.

Molten metal is being poured into a mold for processing.

Above, cooled aluminum blocks are gathered together after casting.

The free electrons also make metals good conductors of heat. If one end of a metal bar is heated, the electrons there move faster. They collide with electrons further away and they, too, move faster. In this way, heat is quickly conducted along the bar.

The free electrons are also responsible for the shiny appearance of most metals. The free electrons prevent the light from entering very far into the metal. The light is reflected.

The atoms in most metals are packed tightly together in regular rows. This is why most metals have a high density. A piece of metal is made up of many tiny crystals.

Like the atoms, these crystals are arranged in a regular order. Defects can occur in the arrangement of both the atoms and the

SOME PROPERTIES AND USES OF METALS

Metal	Symbol	Melting point °C	Relative density	Important properties	Uses
Actinide series **					
Aluminum	Al	660	2.70		Pots and pans, motors, aircraft, electricity and alloys
Antimony	Sb	630	6.69	Poisonous	Used in pewter and type metal
Barium	Ba	725	3.5	Reacts with water	Compounds used in glass and X-ray photography
Beryllium	Be	1283	1.8	Poisonous; hard to work	Used in light, strong alloys and in nuclear reactors as moderator
Bismuth	Bi	271	9.7	Expands on freezing	Used in type metal (see printing) compounds used as sedatives
Cadmium	Cd	321	8.6	Poisonous	Used in easily melted alloys and to coat iron against chemical attack
Calcium	Ca	839	1.5	Reacts slowly with water	Compounds widely used
Cesium	Cs	29	1.87	Reacts explosively with water	
Chromium	Cr	1870	7.19		Used as a coating or alloy to protect steel; compounds used as pigments or oxidizers
Cobalt	Co	1495	8.9	Magnetic	Used in magnetic alloys and high temperature cutting alloys
Copper	Cu	1083	8.96		For electrical conductors and in alloys with tin, zinc, aluminium, etc.
Francium	Fr	27		Radioactive	
Gallium	Ga	30	5.9	Expands on freezing	Used in high temperature thermometers
Germanium	Ge	958	5.46	Hard and brittle	Used in semiconductors
Gold	Au	1063	19.3	Soft and malleable	Used in jewellery, dentistry, and protective or ornamental coatings
Hafnium	Hf	2222	13.3	Difficult to separate from zirconium	Used in nuclear reactor control rods
Indium	In	156	7.3	Wets glass; shrieks when bent	
Iridium	Ir	2443	22.4		Used chiefly as an alloy with platinum, to make the latter harder. This alloy is used in pen points, parts of scientific apparatus, and surgical tools
Iron	Fe	1539	7.87	Magnetic	As steel—the most used metal
Lanthanum	La	920	6.15		
Lead	Pb	328	11.35	Soft, resists corrosion	Used in plumbing (but is poisonous) waterproofing, batteries and low-melting alloys for solder
Lithium	Li	180	0.53	The lightest metal; reacts with water	Compounds used in glass and as high temperature lubricants
Magnesium	Mg	649	1.7	Burns with a bright white flame	Used in lightweight alloys for aircraft
Manganese	Mn	1244	7.3	Hard and brittle	Used in alloy steels
Mercury	Hg	—39	13.5	Liquid at room temperature	Used in thermometers etc.; compounds poisonous and used in insecticides
Molybdenum	Mo	2617	10.2	Hard	Used in very hard alloy steel; sulfide is used as a lubricant
Nickel	Ni	1453	8.9	Slightly magnetic	Used in stainless steel and in alloys for coinage
Niobium	Nb	2468	8.57		Improves the strength of alloy steels

crystals. When this happens, one layer of atoms or crystals can easily slide over the next layer. This means that the metal can easily change its shape. However, as it changes its shape, new defects are produced. In time, these defects weaken the metal and it becomes brittle. The defects can be removed by heating the metal. (*See* HEAT TREATMENT.)

Most pure metals are soft. They can be strengthened by combining them with other metals. These combinations of metals are called alloys. (*See* ALLOY.) Typical alloys are brass, which contains copper and zinc, and bronze, which contains copper and tin. Steel is an unusual alloy. It contains iron with a small amount of a nonmetallic element, carbon. Usually, steel also contains small amounts of other metals as well.

SOME PROPERTIES AND USES OF METALS

Metal	Symbol	Melting point °C	Relative density	Important properties	Uses
Osmium	Os	3050	22.7	Heaviest metal	Salts used to stain living tissues
Palladium	Pd	1552	12.0	Absorbs 900 times its volume of hydrogen	Used as a catalyst
Platinum	Pt	1772	21.5		Used in jewellery, laboratory vessels, temperature measurement, etc.
Polonium	Po	254	9.3	Radioactive	
Potassium	K	63	0.86	Catches fire in water; slightly radioactive	Compounds used as fertilizers
Radium	Ra	700	5.0	Radioactive	Used in cancer treatment
Rare Earth Metals*					
Rhenium	Re	3180	21.0		Used in alloys with molybdenum
Rhodium	Rh	1966	12.4		Used in alloys with platinum
Rubidium	Rb	39	1.53	Somewhat radioactive; bursts into fire in air or water	
Ruthenium	Ru	2300	12.4		Used in alloys with platinum
Silver	Ag	961	10.5	Very good electrical conductor	Used in photography, coinage and hard solder
Sodium	Na	98	0.97	Reacts with water	Compounds include common salt, soda, borax and some fertilizers
Strontium	Sr	769	2.54	Reacts with water; powder bursts into fire in air	Compounds used in fireworks
Tantalum	Ta	2996	16.6	Very hard, but can be drawn into a wire	Used in strong alloys with high melting points
Technetium	Tc	2172	11.5	Radioactive	
Tellurium	Te	450	6.2	Combines with gold and silver in nature; poor electrical conductor	
Thallium	Tl	304	11.8	Soft; reacts with water	Compounds poisonous and used to kill rats
Tin	Sn	232	7.3		Used on cans to protect steel; alloyed in soft solder pewter and bronze
Titanium	Ti	1660	4.5	Lightweight	Used in alloys for aircraft; oxide in paints
Tungsten	W	3410	19.3	Highest melting point	Used in electric lights and hard alloy steels
Vanadium	V	1890	6.1	Soft; resists attack by chemicals	Used in tough steels for springs and high-speed tools
Zinc	Zn	420	7.13		Used to protect iron (galvanizing) and in brass and other alloys
Zirconium	Zr	1850	6.5		Used to coat nuclear fuels, oxide used in containers that must withstand heat shock

* see entries DYSPROSIUM, ERBIUM, EUROPIUM, GADOLINIUM, HOLMIUM, LUTETIUM, NEODYMIUM, PRASEODYMIUM, PROMETHIUM, SAMARIUM, SCANDIUM, TERBIUM, THULIUM, YTTERBIUM, YTTRIUM

** see entries ACTINIUM, AMERICIUM, BERKELIUM, CALIFORNIUM, CURIUM, EINSTEINIUM, FERMIUM, HAHNIUM, LAWRENCIUM, MENDELEVIUM, NEPTUNIUM, PLUTONIUM, PROTACTINIUM, THORIUM, URANIUM

Most metals readily form chemical compounds with other substances. The only exceptions are the noble metals such as gold and platinum. (*See* NOBLE METAL.) Except for the noble metals, all metals combine with the oxygen in the air. This reaction produces a coating of the metal oxide on the surface of the metal. Some of these coatings are very useful. They protect the metal from corrosion. For example, aluminum forms a thin hard coating which sticks firmly to the surface. The coating protects the aluminum from further attack by oxygen. Rust is an oxide coating formed on the surface of iron. However rust is a loose substance and does not stop the oxygen from attacking the iron underneath. Therefore iron and steel must be protected from the air by other means. The iron or steel can be painted or it can be covered with another metal. Iron covered with zinc is called galvanized iron. (*See* GALVANIZING.) Or it can be covered with chromium. The chromium forms a protective layer of oxide. Steel can also be protected by adding a metal throughout the steel. Usually the metal is chromium.

If metals are stretched a little and then released, they return to their original shape. This is called elasticity. (*See* ELASTICITY.) When they are stretched beyond a certain point, they usually stay stretched. This point is called the yield point or the elastic limit. The yield point varies from metal to metal. It also depends on the number of defects in the metal. Lead, for example, has a very low yield point. A brittle metal, such as antimony, has no yield point. It breaks before becoming permanently stretched. Many metals can be deformed by a large amount before they break. These metals can be easily rolled into sheets or drawn out into wires.

In order to produce a metal object, the metal has to be shaped. There are a number of different ways of doing this. One common method is called casting. The metal is first heated until it melts. Then it is poured into a mold of the right shape. In another method, the metal is heated but not allowed to melt. The metal is then forced by pressure into molds. These molds are called dies. Wire is made by pulling metal through a number of holes in turn. Each hole is smaller than the last. In this way, the diameter of the wire is slowly reduced until it is the right size. Metal sheets are made by squeezing the metal between heavy rollers.

A modern method of shaping metal is called sintering. In sintering, powdered metal is used. The powdered metal is pressed into the correct shape in a mold. The particles in the powder are then joined together by heating. Sometimes pressure is used as well.

Above, part of a copper refining plant. Metals are produced here in a pure state by electrolysis, a way of separating the metal by passing an electric current through a liquid compound.

Left, platinum gauzes up to 3.6 meters [12 feet] in width can be woven on looms. Such gauzes are used as catalysts in the production of nitric acid from ammonia. Pure metals can be shaped and used in a great variety of ways.

Metal atoms are packed together like these bearings.

Some products made of gold, silver and platinum.

Above, an aluminum conductor being extruded through a die.

Metallurgy Metallurgy (met′ əl ər′ jē) is the study of metals and alloys. The most important branch of metallurgy is the study of the methods of extracting metals from the earth. Most metals occur only as compounds in minerals. Only a few, such as gold, are found uncombined. Minerals that are mined for their metals are called ores. (*See* ORE.) Ores usually contain a mixture of different minerals. The amount of metal in an ore can vary greatly. Most iron is obtained from an ore that is almost pure iron oxide. Gold ore, on the other hand, may only contain one part of gold in a million.

The first step is to crush the ore. Then the material containing the metal is separated from the rest of the ore. The unwanted material is called the gangue. The material containing the metal is called the concentrate. There are various methods of obtaining the metal from the concentrate. The method used depends on the metal.

One common method is to heat the concentrate in air. The oxygen in the air converts the metal into the metal oxide. Usually the oxide is then heated with carbon and a flux in a furnace. The carbon removes the oxygen from the oxide and forms the gas carbon dioxide. This leaves behind the melted metal. The flux combines with other impurities in the concentrate. The impurities form a slag. Because the metals are heavy, the slag floats on top of the molten metal. The slag is then skimmed off. This method is used for metals such as iron and lead.

Some ores are treated with an acid or some other substance. The substance combines with the metal to form a compound. The compound can be extracted by dissolving it in water. Gold is sometimes extracted by this method.

The other common method is electrolysis. (*See* ELECTROLYSIS.) This method is used for very reactive metals such as aluminum and sodium. In electrolysis, a compound of the metal is heated until it melts. An electric current is then passed through the liquid. The current enters and leaves the liquid through electrodes. As the current flows, pure metal is deposited onto one of the electrodes.

M.E./R.W.L.

METAL FATIGUE (met′ əl fə tēg′) If too heavy a load is put on a piece of metal, it breaks. If a lighter load is put on the metal, it does not immediately break. However, a light load can weaken the metal. Eventually, the metal can become so weak that it breaks. This is called metal fatigue.

In general, metal fatigue is caused by forces called stresses. A load is an example of a stress. Another example is a straight piece of metal that has been slightly bent. The bending causes a stress in the metal. If a metal is under stress, very small cracks start to appear on the surface. These cracks become bigger and move inwards. Then they start to join up with one another. Eventually the cracks weaken the metal so much that it breaks.

Metal fatigue is particularly dangerous in aircraft. It has caused a number of crashes. Today, certain metal parts in aircraft are regularly tested for cracks. If the part is cracked, it is replaced. This helps to prevent metal fatigue. There are other methods of preventing metal fatigue. Metal parts can be redesigned to reduce the stress. New fatigue-resistant metals have been developed. Another method is to treat the surface of the metal. This can help to stop the cracks from forming.

M.E./J.T.

METALWORK (met′ əl wərk′) Metal work is the technology of preparing metals to make useful objects. It includes the craft of making decorative objects.

A student learns the technique of welding pieces of metal together.

Metals are often cast into blocks, or ingots. These can be squeezed between rollers to make flat sheets, or the rollers can be designed to produce other shapes. Tubes or rods of aluminum and copper are usually made by extrusion. In extrusion, a cylinder-shaped block of hot metal is squeezed through a small hole or between a central rod and a cylindrical wall.

Metal shapes are often forged. Drop forging is one of the most common types of forging in large factories. A heavy hammer carries a mold of the upper half of the desired shape. The lower half mold of the desired shape is fixed to an anvil below the hammer. A piece of metal is placed on the anvil, and the hammer is brought down with great force. This action produces the desired shape. Many large metal parts are shaped this way.

All these processes are carried out with metal that is hot and relatively soft. Finely detailed work is done with cold metal. For example, wire is made by drawing metal blocks through dies that have successively smaller holes. A die is an extra hard metal device that contains a mold of the desired shape. It shapes the metal because it is harder than the metal being drawn through it. Dies are used to stamp out buttons, medals, and other small articles from flat sheets of metal. Hydraulic presses are used to stamp out automobile body parts.

Parts made from metal can be joined together mechanically with rivets or bolts and nuts. However, welding is the most common method of joining metal objects. Brazing and soldering are two other types of metal joining. Welding is stronger and more permanent than brazing and soldering.

Metals are machined for a smooth, shiny finish. They are ground and polished with hard tools and abrasive powders.

W.R.P./R.W.L.

METAMORPHIC ROCK (met′ ə mȯr′ fik räk) Metamorphic rock is rock that has changed in appearance or composition. The changes are caused by heat, pressure, and chemical changes beneath the earth's surface. Metamorphic rocks reach the surface by upliftings and other movements of the earth's crust.

Changes in rocks due to heat are called contact metamorphism. Contact metamorphism occurs when magma heats the rocks surrounding it. (*See* MAGMA.) The rocks are baked and hardened by the heat. A circle of metamorphic rocks called an aureole often forms around a pocket of magma. (*See* BATHOLITH.)

Some metamorphic rocks are formed by a process called hydrothermal metamorphism. Hydrothermal metamorphism occurs when chemically active gases and liquids are released from magma. The gases and liquids change the chemical composition of the pre-existing rock.

Metamorphic rocks often form by a process called dynamic metamorphism. Dynamic metamorphism occurs when rocks are ground and crushed by tremendous pressure. The minerals in the rocks, although rearranged, are not chemically changed.

Dynamothermal metamorphism occurs when heat and pressure combine to change rocks. Dynamothermal rocks include marble, gneiss, and slate. J.M.C./W.R.S.

METAMORPHOSIS (met′ ə mȯr′ fə səs) Metamorphosis is a series of changes in structure through which some organisms progress between birth and adulthood. It is controlled by special hormones. (*See* HORMONE.) The word "metamorphosis" comes from the Greek meaning "to transform." Many amphibians go through metamorphosis from egg to tadpole to adult. (*See* FROG.) Sponges and some fish also undergo metamorphosis.

All insects undergo metamorphosis. It may be complete metamorphosis or incomplete metamorphosis. In complete metamorphosis, the insect goes through four stages:

egg, larva, pupa, and adult. The larva is usually not at all like the adult in appearance, behavior, or living environment. (*See* LARVA.) It increases its size by molting, or shedding its skin, several times before becoming a pupa. The pupa usually is more like the adult in appearance. Many of the adult structures, such as wings, have begun to develop. The most striking examples of complete metamorphosis are those of butterflies and moths. (*See* BUTTERFLY AND MOTH.)

Incomplete metamorphosis (or gradual metamorphosis) includes three stages of development: egg, nymph (or naiad), and adult. The nymph looks like a small adult, but is born wingless. (*See* NYMPH.) After the first molt, small wings appear as flaps of skin on the back. With each successive molt, the wings continue to develop until fully formed in the adult. Nymphs, like larvae, often have different behavior and living environments from the adults. The grasshopper is a good example of an insect which undergoes incomplete metamorphosis. (*See* GRASSHOPPER.) *See also* AMPHIBIAN; INSECT; MOLTING.

A.J.C./E.R.L.

Frog tadpoles lie clustered on top of jelly, one day after hatching from it.

METAZOA (met′ ə zō′ ə) The animal kingdom is divided into three subkingdoms: Protozoa, Parazoa, and Metazoa. Protozoa are all one-celled animals. Parazoa are all sponges. Metazoa are all other multicellular animals. *See also* ANIMAL KINGDOM. A.J.C./E.R.L.

METCHNIKOFF, ÉLIE (1845–1916) Élie Metchnikoff (mech′ nē kŏf) was a Russian biologist. He discovered a process called phagocytosis. All blood contains cells called white corpuscles. When a foreign body such as a bacterium enters the blood, it is attacked by a white corpuscle. The corpuscle surrounds the body and absorbs it. This kills the foreign body. Metchnikoff called this process phagocytosis. Cells that can surround and absorb bodies he called phagocytes. Phagocytosis is very important in the body's fight against infection. (*See* IMMUNITY.) For this discovery, Metchnikoff shared the 1908 Nobel Prize for Medicine and Physiology with Paul Ehrlich. (*See* EHRLICH, PAUL.) Metchnikoff also suggested that phagocytes could sometimes attack a person's own body cells. This was later discovered to be true.

M.E./D.G.F.

Élie Metchnikoff

METEOR (mēt′ ē ər) A meteor is a streak of light caused by a chunk of metal or rock entering the earth's atmosphere from outer space. The particle is called a meteoroid until it reaches the earth's surface. If the meteoroid hits the earth's surface, it is called a meteorite.

Meteorites orbit the sun and are considered members of the solar system. They are composed of metallic or stony matter. When a meteoroid approaches the earth, it gets caught in the earth's gravitational field. (*See* GRAVITY.) As it enters the atmosphere, the heat caused by friction may heat the meteoroid to 2,200°C [4,000°F]. This heat causes the meteoroid to glow. Most meteoroids burn up

A meteor crater in Arizona, formed more than 12,000 years ago.

completely at altitudes of 48 to 80 km [30 to 50 mi]. Only the largest meteoroids reach the earth's surface.

No one is sure where meteoroids come from. Some may form from shattered asteroids or moons. Others may originate from comets. About 25 million visible meteoroids enter the earth's atmosphere every day.

Meteorites Meteorites are huge meteoroids that have reached the earth's surface. They are usually very large, since small meteoroids burn up before reaching the surface.

There are three main types of meteorites. Stony meteorites, called aerolites, contain stony minerals. Iron meteorites, called siderites, contain mostly iron and nickel. Meteorites which contain a mixture of stone and iron are called siderolites.

Meteorites are of great interest to scientists. Until the lunar landings, they were the only source of material from outer space. (*See* MOON.) Astronomers have gained valuable knowledge about the formation of the universe by studying meteorites. (*See* COSMOLOGY.)

Meteor showers When the earth passes through a swarm of meteoroids, bright sparks and streaks in the sky form a meteor shower. No known meteorites have resulted from meteor showers. The meteoroids of a meteor shower are probably fragments of comets. Meteor showers are named for the constellation from which they seem to radiate. There are several meteor showers that occur about the same time each year. For example, the Leonid meteor shower, which seems to radiate from the constellation Leo, occurs about November 17 each year. *See also* COMET. J.M.C./C.R.

The line across the bottom left of this picture is the trail of a meteor. A comet with its bright tail can be seen bottom right.

METEOROLOGY (mēt′ ē ə räl′ ə jē) Meteorology is the study of the atmosphere. Because all weather occurs in the troposphere (the lowest level of the atmosphere), meteorology is also the study of the weather.

Weather is the condition of the atmosphere at a given time in one place. Climate is the sum of all weather conditions over a long period of time. Climate takes into account averages of temperature, precipitation, and wind. Weather is constantly changing; climate changes slowly over long periods of time. Weather and climate affect the way people dress, how they live, what kinds of work they do, and the food they eat.

Meteorologists use chemistry, physics, and mathematics in their work. Chemistry is used when studying the gases that make up the atmosphere. Meteorologists analyze smog and other forms of air pollution using chemical principles. (*See* POLLUTION.)

Physics is closely related to meteorology. Physical changes in the atmosphere cause the weather to occur. Through physics, meteorologists can explain precipitation (such as rain and snow), lightning and other atmospheric phenomena. Using mathematics, meteorologists can measure and forecast the movements of weather systems.

Meteorological instruments The meteorologist uses many instruments to study the atmosphere. The most common instrument is the thermometer, which measures the air temperature. A barometer is used to measure the atmospheric (barometric) pressure. A drop in pressure often tells the approach of stormy weather. A rise in pressure indicates a period of good weather.

The wind is measured by an instrument called an anemometer. A hygrometer is used to measure the amount of water vapor in the air. (*See* HUMIDITY.) A rain gauge is used to measure the amount of rainfall.

A radiosonde is a balloon that is sent up into the atmosphere. It takes measurements at different atmospheric levels. The information is then sent back to the earth. The wind velocity and other data sent from a radiosonde can be used to forecast the development and movement of weather systems. (*See* JET STREAM.)

Weather satellites have been orbiting the earth since 1959. The satellites take photographs (*opposite page*) which are sent back to earth. Meteorologists use the photographs to study developing weather systems. Satellites have been especially useful in tracking hurricanes and tropical storms.

The history of meteorology For many centuries, people thought the weather was under the control of various gods. If the weather was good, the gods were rewarding the people. Violent weather was considered the anger of the gods.

Modern meteorology began with the invention of the thermometer and the barometer in the 1600s. By the late 1700s, scientists realized that the weather was associated with moving air systems. With the development of the telegraph in 1844, weather information could be collected for the preparation of forecasts. In the early 1900s, radio made it possible for ships to exchange information on the weather.

About the time of World War I, a group of Norwegian meteorologists developed the polar front theory. This theory shows how storms tend to form in the region where the cold polar air meets the warm subtropical air. This region is called the polar front. (*See* CYCLONE; FRONT.)

In 1922, Lewis Fry Richardson related temperature, humidity, and other factors to weather forecasting. Patterns could be observed based on changes in one or more of the factors. Similar patterns often lead to similar weather.

Richardson also devised a grid system for covering the world in segments, with a weather observation station in the center of

each segment. The observation stations would be used to accumulate information about current weather conditions from all over the world. Then forecasting could be done with greater accuracy. Regularly spaced weather stations would provide highly accurate forecasts. However, only about 15 percent of the surface of the earth is currently monitored regularly for weather data, and most of that monitoring takes place in the northern hemisphere.

Since World War II, meteorologists have benefited from rapid technological advances. Radar is used to monitor storm systems. In some parts of the world, regularly spaced radar stations monitor large areas. Meteorologists can trace the progress of the systems and track rainfall.

Meteorologists have had access to a global view of atmospheric conditions because of the satellites that have been shot into space since 1959. Weather satellites take photographs which are transmitted back to earth. A progression of photographs shows developing weather systems all over the world.

Two kinds of weather satellites transmit weather information—polar satellites and geostationary satellites. The polar satellites circle the earth over both of the poles. Their orbits shift along the equator as the earth rotates. Because of the gradual shifting of their orbits, polar satellites take photos of the entire surface of the earth once every twelve hours. Geostationary satellites are positioned in orbit over one area of the earth; they are stationary relative to the earth's rotation, and concentrate their coverage on that one area.

Advances in technology will soon make it possible for satellites or space stations to monitor wind speeds, barometric pressures, and temperatures just as the radiosondes now do at lower levels.

The key to using the data provided by radiosondes, radar, satellites, and a network of weather observation stations is the computer. High-speed computers are able to absorb millions of pieces of data and translate them into meaningful information with which meteorologists can forecast weather.

In the United States, weather forecasts are made by the National Weather Service. Forecasts are based on over 40,000 observations made on the earth each day, plus the information coming from satellites, ships, weather balloons, and aircraft. All of this information is gathered together in a large computer facility at the National Meteorological Center in Maryland, near Washington, D.C. Twice daily, national forecasts are sent to 52 regional weather service offices. Local meteorologists use the available data on nearby conditions to interpret the local forecasts. Then the local forecasts are printed in newspapers or are broadcast on radio and television. These forecasts are known as "convenience forecasts."

In addition to local forecasts, the National Weather Service also provides agricultural forecasts regarding farming, ranching, and related industries; aviation forecasts for private and commercial aircraft; and marine forecasts about conditions on oceans and lakes. Many private forecasting services also operate to give specialized data to business and industry. *See also* ATMOSPHERE; WEATHER.   J.M.C./C.R.

METER-KILOGRAM-SECOND SYSTEM The meter-kilogram-second (mēt′ ər kē′ lə gram sek′ ənd) system is a system of units used by scientists. It is usually called the mks system. It uses the meter as the unit of length. The kilogram is the unit of mass or weight. The second is the unit of time. It has now almost completely replaced the older foot-pound-second system in science. (*See* FOOT-POUND-SECOND SYSTEM.) The mks system is a part of the SI or International System of Units. (*See* INTERNATIONAL SYSTEM.) SI units use the mks system and various electrical and magnetic units as well. *See also* CALIBRATION; UNIT.   M.E./R.W.L.

METHANE (meth′ ān′) Methane (CH_4) is a colorless, odorless gas. It is flammable and gives off a large amount of heat when it burns. Natural gas is mostly methane. Natural gas is used as a fuel. Methane is also found in marsh gas and coal gas. It also occurs in firedamp. Firedamp is a mixture of explosive gases and is found in coal mines. It is very dangerous because it explodes very easily.

Other than as a fuel, methane is used to make other chemicals. It combines with chlorine to form chloroform and carbon tetrachloride. It can be oxidized to give methyl alcohol (methanol) and formaldehyde. (*See* OXIDATION AND REDUCTION.) Methane can also be burned to form a substance called carbon black, a form of carbon used as a black pigment. M.E./J.M.

METRIC SYSTEM

The metric system (me′ trik sis′ təm) is a group of units used to measure various properties, such as length, weight, temperature, and time. In the 1790s a group of French scientists created the metric system. At various times this system has undergone changes. The official title of the present system is called the International System of Units, abbreviated as SI.

To someone who has not used it, the metric system may at first seem difficult to understand. The difficulty comes from the need to convert measurements in the units of one system into the units of the other. Once a person gets used to the metric system, he or she usually finds it very easy to use. The metric system is simple to use for two main reasons. First, it follows the decimal number system. In other words, units in the metric system increase or decrease in size by 10. For example, a meter has 10 parts called decimeters. A decimeter has 10 parts called centimeters. Units in the customary system, also called the English system, do not follow a simple number system. Feet and yards are related by 3s. But feet and inches are related by 12s. Second, the metric system has only seven basic units that make up all its measurements. The customary system uses more than twenty basic units. Seven basic units form the foundation of the metric system; four of these units are commonly used.

1. The meter is the base unit for length or distance. A meter is a little longer than a yard. Shorter lengths are measured in centimeters or millimeters. A centimeter equals about 0.4 inches. A pencil may be measured in centimeters. A millimeter is equal to about 0.04 inches. Tiny mechanical parts are often measured in millimeters. Long distances, such as those between towns, are measured in kilometers. A kilometer is equal to about 0.621 miles. A shorter distance, such as the height of flagpole, is measured in meters.

A surface measurement tells how much area something covers. Many areas, such as that of a floor, are measured in square meters. A square meter is equal to the surface covered by a square one meter long on each side. A square meter is slightly larger than a square yard. Square centimeters or square millimeters may be used to measure smaller areas. Land may be measured in units called hectares. A hectare equals about 10,000 square meters, or roughly 2.5 acres. Some land areas may be measured in square kilometers. Volume and capacity measurements tell how much space something occupies. Volume and capacity are both measured in cubic units, such as cubic meters or cubic centimeters. Most capacity measurements for liquids are made in units called liters. A liter, equal to a cubic decimeter, is a little larger than a liquid quart. Smaller units include the milliliter, which equals a cubic centimeter.

2. The kilogram is the base unit of mass.

(*See* MASS.) It equals about 2.2 avoirdupois pounds in the customary system. The gram is used for smaller measurements. A gram equals 0.001 kilogram. Bulk goods are weighed in metric tons. A metric ton equals 1,000 kilograms. A metric ton equals about 1.1 "short" tons in the customary system.

3. The second is the base unit for time. The metric system measures time exactly as the customary system does for measurements longer than a second. (*See* TIME.)

4. The kelvin is the unit for temperature. Most people use Celsius temperatures instead of kelvin temperature. One degree kelvin equals one degree Celsius. But the two temperature scales begin at different points. (*See* CELSIUS SCALE; KELVIN SCALE.) Water freezes at 0°C [32°F] or 273.15K and boils at 100°C [212°F] or 373.15K. Celsius has been the official name of the metric scale for temperature since 1948.

The three other base units for measurement in the metric system are the ampere, the mole, and the candela. The ampere is a base unit for electrical measurements. The mole is the base unit for measuring the amount of any substance involved in a chemical or other reaction. The candela is the base unit for measuring light. (*See* AMPERE; CANDELA; MOLE.)

In 1975, the United States Congress passed a bill that formed a policy of voluntary conversion to the metric system. The U.S. Metric Board was formed to develop and carry out a program of gradual conversion. The use of metric units is on a consistent increase in business and industry. In time, the metric system is expected to replace the customary system of measurement in the United States.

The table below shows a way to convert some basic units in the two systems of measurement. Such conversions give only close approximations.   J.J.A./R.W.L.

	TO CONVERT	INTO	MULTIPLY BY
lengths **and** **distances:**	inches (in)	millimeters (mm)	25
	feet (ft)	centimeters (cm)	30
	yards (yd)	meters (m)	0.9
	miles (mi)	kilometers (km)	1.6
	millimeters (mm)	inches (in)	0.04
	centimeters (cm)	inches (in)	0.4
	meters (m)	yards (yd)	1.1
	kilometers (km)	miles (mi)	0.6
volume **and** **capacity:**	fluid ounces (fl oz)	milliliters (ml)	30
	pints, U.S. (pt)	liters (l)	0.47
	quarts, U.S. (qt)	liters (l)	0.95
	gallons, U.S. (gal)	liters (l)	3.8
	milliliters (ml)	fluid ounces (fl oz)	0.034
	liters (l)	pints, U.S. (pt)	2.1
	liters (l)	quarts, U.S. (qt)	1.06
	liters (l)	gallons, U.S. (gal)	0.26
weight **and** **mass:**	ounces (oz)	grams (g)	28
	pounds (lb)	kilograms (kg)	0.45
	short tons	metric tons (t)	0.9
	grams (g)	ounces (oz)	0.035
	kilograms (kg)	pounds (lb)	2.2
	metric tons (t)	short tons	1.1
temperature:	degrees Fahrenheit (°F)	degrees Celsius (°C)	0.56 (after subtracting 32)
	degrees Celsius (°C)	degrees Fahrenheit (°F)	1.8 (then add 32)
area:	acres	hectares (ha)	0.4
	hectares (ha)	acres	2.5